dynamic PSYCHIATRY
IN SIMPLE TERMS

dynamic PSYCHIATRY
IN SIMPLE TERMS

by
ROBERT R. MEZER, M.D.
Formerly Instructor in Psychiatry, Harvard Medical School, and Assistant Professor of Psychiatry, Boston University School of Medicine

Foreword by
Harry C. Solomon, M.D.

Fourth Edition

 SPRINGER Publishing Company, Inc.
New York, N.Y.

First Edition 1956

Second Edition 1960

Third Edition 1967

Fourth Edition 1970

Copyright © 1970

SPRINGER PUBLISHING COMPANY, INC.

200 Park Avenue South, New York, N.Y. 10003

Library of Congress Catalog Card Number: 75-102898

Printed in U.S.A.

Foreword

When psychiatry teachers get together it is a frequent
occurrence for each to bemoan the lack of a satisfactory textbook on the subject. This occurs whether the students be
in medicine, nursing or social work. Many teachers threaten
to write a book which will present the subject according to
their own viewpoint. Whether because of indolence, caution
or the recognition of the difficulty of doing the job well, few
make the attempt. Among these few is the author of the
present small book. After some years of experience in teaching the subject to medical students, nursing students and
social workers, Dr. Mezer has shown the initiative, energy
and temerity to put in printed words the material as he has
presented it to these student groups. The presentation has
the virtue of departing from the conventional method of the
standard text. The author attempts to portray the growth
and development of the individual in the framework of
psychoanalytic thought, simplifying the theories and observations and expressing them in plain English. He presents
the classical psychiatric concepts and the standard classifica-
tions also in his own method, in his own words and without
much of the stereotypy which has been conventional. He
gives a brief critical review of the care of the hospitalized
patient and the treatment methods, both psychological and
somatic. The text is written in a simple and readable form,
without attempts at erudition; it is not full of quotations,
annotations and references. It is evident, however, that in
order to find the simple form of presentation, Dr. Mezer

must have read widely, thought deeply and distilled what to him appears to be the essence of the subject.

It may be asked whether, because of the author's long teaching connection with the Harvard Medical School and the Boston Psychopathic Hospital, the book represents the viewpoint of his associates. The answer to the question is that neither the medical school faculty nor the hospital faculty has a uniform, rigid system. Each member of these faculties undoubtedly will differ with certain statements made in the text; I would presume that the difference would be, in large part, a matter of detail—some would differ in the emphasis given to somatic treatments, whereas others of the staff would view the emphasis on the dynamic aspects as perhaps undue in amount.

HARRY C. SOLOMON, M.D.

Former Commissioner of Mental Health,
Commonwealth of Massachusetts;
Professor Emeritus of Psychiatry,
Harvard Medical School

Preface to the Fourth Edition

This fourth edition has been completely revised to reflect the changes of nomenclature in the new edition of the *Diagnostic and Statistical Manual of Mental Disorders*. The chapter on mental retardation and organic brain syndromes has been rewritten and expanded. More emphasis is given to community psychiatry and to the chemical treatment of mental illness. The current drug abuse problem is dealt with in Chapter 7 in the section on organic brain syndromes and again in Chapter 10 in the section on alcoholism and drug dependence. The bibliography also has been updated. It is hoped that these changes and revisions will keep this book abreast of recent developments while increasing its usefulness to the reader.

ROBERT ROSS MEZER, M.D.

Boston
November, 1969

From the Preface to the First Edition

The wish to write this book grew out of several years of lecturing to medical students and student nurses undergoing their psychiatric affiliation, out of giving courses to many different groups on social hygiene and on bringing up children, and out of a feeling, purely personal, that psychiatry can be made understandable. I do not, therefore, regard this book as a contribution to the field of psychiatry —unless helping people to understand psychiatry can be considered a contribution. Thus, the object everywhere has been to get at the basic principles of what may be called "dynamic psychiatry" and present them in easily understandable terms, taking only as few liberties with theory and details as appear necessary to maintain simplicity.

Many authors of psychiatric books and papers will find that ideas and conclusions of theirs were utilized and adapted to the scheme of this presentation. Familiar concepts, suddenly seen in a light of fewer nuances and crowded into a small orbit, may appear unusual and even new.

The book is so planned—its ideas are so developed—that it is best read from cover to cover. Subheadings were left out in order to keep the whole story going rather than draw attention to its parts. The student may then want to re-read the book in its entirety while branching out into the literature given with every chapter.

R. R. M.

GENERAL BIBLIOGRAPHY

The books included here, most of them textbooks, are each referred to in many of the reading lists following the chapters of this book. Detailed bibliographic data are given below, whereas in the reading lists these titles are stated in brief form, followed by references to the relevant sections of the books.

Abraham, K. *Selected Papers on Psychoanalysis,* Third American edition. New York: Basic Books, 1957.

Batchelor, I. *Henderson and Gillespie's Textbook of Psychiatry for Students and Practitioners,* Tenth edition. London: Oxford University Press, 1969.

Diagnostic and Statistical Manual of Mental Disorders, Second edition. American Psychiatric Assn., 1700 18th St., N.W., Washington, D.C. 20009, 1968.

English, O. S., and Pearson, H. H. J. *Common Neuroses of Children and Adults.* New York: W. W. Norton, 1964.

Ewalt, J. R., and Farnsworth, D. L. *Textbook of Psychiatry.* New York: The Blakiston Division, McGraw-Hill Book Co., 1963.

Fenichel, O. *Psychoanalytic Theory of Neurosis.* New York: W. W. Norton, 1945.

Freud, S. *The Standard Edition of the Complete Psychological Works of Sigmund Freud.* Translated by James Strachey. London: Hogarth Press, 1966.

Hendrick, I. *Facts and Theories of Psychoanalysis,* Third edition. New York: A. A. Knopf, 1958. Also published in paperback: Dell Publishing Company, 1966.

Kolb, L. C. *Noyes' Modern Clinical Psychiatry,* Seventh edition. Philadelphia: W. B. Saunders Co., 1968.

Contents

PART I

Introduction

CHAPTER 1

Meeting the Psychiatric Patient

Of the many definitions of psychiatry now in use, the
one most widely applied defines psychiatry as the study of
human personality with emphasis on providing professional
help to the disturbed and unhappy members of our society.
An important term in this definition which must be explained is the word *personality*. Let us imagine a man who
finds himself on the railroad tracks with a train coming at
him. He can act in several different ways: he can lie down
and let the train run over him, he can run away in a fit of
panic, or he can simply step off the track and let the train
go on its merry way. Or imagine a girl at a dance who breaks
the strap of her brassière: she can blush with embarrassment,
she can go quietly to the ladies' room and fix it, or she can
decide never to go to a dance again. It might be said that
situations impose themselves upon an individual and give
rise to reactions. Personality, which psychiatry defines as the
sum of an individual's reactions, is what makes the world
interesting, for it includes the responses of innumerable
individuals to innumerable situations.

To size up, to assess a personality is a technical process
known as "doing a mental status on a patient," and this is
the psychiatric equivalent of the physical examination in

3

medicine. Every patient admitted to a medical ward is given an examination from which the doctor learns his blood pressure, pulse rate, rate of respiration, and so on—all in order to assess physical status. Psychiatry is concerned with mental or personality status, and the method of assessment is different from that used in medicine because no instruments are necessary—only the ability to observe and to think are involved.

An excellent way to grasp the psychiatric method of assessing personality is to think of two persons meeting on the street; they, too, do a mental status. Clearly, the first thing one sees in another person is his *appearance,* and that is the first factor recorded in a mental status. Psychiatrists want to determine whether the patient is neatly or sloppily dressed, whether his clothes are appropriate or more like a masquerade costume, his hair is neat or messy, his nails manicured or ragged and dirty. All such factors make up his personal appearance.

The second item is *behavior.* Actions make up behavior and must be noted. Does the patient walk in a normal way, or scratch his head with every third step, or climb every lamp post in sight? Psychiatrists are interested not only in quality of behavior—such as the peculiarities of actions just described—but also in the amount or quantity of behavior. Is the patient over- or underactive? He may not move at all, or he may be unable to sit still.

In an encounter on the street, after noticing the other person's appearance and behavior, one will proceed to ask, "How are you?" or "How are you feeling?" which really means, "What's your mood today?" So the third factor in doing a mental status is *mood.* Used in this way the word is almost new to most people, though by definition it means feeling; psychiatry has another word with the same connotation, *affect.* For all practical purposes the two have the same meaning, but a subtle difference does exist in that affect stands for the quantity, and mood for the quality of a patient's feeling. The words are interchangeable in general usage; if affect is heard more often than mood in psychiatric circles, it is mainly because it forms a usable adjective. Affective sounds all right, but moody has a meaning of its own, and neither mooded nor moodic sounds like English. The quality of a patient's mood is depressed when he is sad, and manic when he is overly happy. The terms "affectless" and "bland" are used if drive and energy are deficient, but when affect is like most people's, it is termed normal. Mood is frequently termed inappropriate when the affect or mood accompanying a thought is unsuitable; for example, if a patient laughs at the thought that his mother has died.

The fourth action of two people on meeting is to begin a conversation; hence, *speech* is the fourth factor in the mental status. The psychiatrist observes whether the patient talks about things one can understand or about an imaginary world. Is his speech so confused that it doesn't make any sense; that is, do his words come out clearly enough, but still mean nothing? Or, does he make up his own words? Is he witty, filthy, or profane? Does he often refer to Christ, God, or to religious matters in general? Such factors constitute the quality of speech. Psychiatrists are equally interested in its quantity. It is often said that women talk more than men, yet nurses in mental wards see many male patients who put women to shame in this respect. Some talk a mile a minute, for this is a part of their illness. Psychiatrists need to determine whether the patient has a normal quantity of speech.

The fifth component of a person's mental status is his *thinking*. Since thought usually determines speech, the two might be termed inseparable, were it not for the fact that people often think things which they do not say. In this separate category for thinking, again, both quality and quantity are observed. Thinking quality is of interest because there are illnesses which produce erratic or abstruse thinking quite impossible to figure out. Delusions are one important type of aberration in the quality of thinking; for example, the patient is convinced that he is being persecuted when there is no real basis for his belief. As far as quantity is concerned, psychiatrists must know whether so many thoughts come to the patient that one almost pushes the other out of his head, or if he thinks so slowly that none seem to come at all. Thinking is synonymous with mental content.

A sixth factor is *memory,* of which there are three kinds, recent, remote and immediate. Recent memory pertains to the past hour, day, week or year; remote memory deals with things far away in time, like the patient's first year in school or his eighth or his twelfth year of age; immediate memory refers to his immediate recall of something. Can he remember a telephone number immediately after hearing it, or the name of a person he has just met? These types of memory may be afflicted separately or in combination in different illnesses.

There are many definitions of *intelligence,* but the most common defines it as simply the ability to reason, to use logic. This innate ability is a basic component—the seventh —of human personality, and is measured in terms of the I.Q. (Intelligence Quotient) for which a great variety of tests exist. Psychiatrists are interested in two more factors of the personality: eighth—*orientation,* the patient's ability to know who he is, where he is, and when the present moment is taking place. He should know his own name, be aware that he is in a hospital and not a church or auditorium, and as far as time is concerned should know that this is 1970, that it's May, that summer is coming, and that it's daytime, although not necessarily the exact time of day. Ninth—*judgment,* the patient's ability to size up a situation and to act appropriately, is often difficult to evaluate. Judgment may be equated with commonsense. The examiner can subjectively evaluate judgment in terms of what the patient has done or said, or he can test it by the more objective (but perhaps less significant) method of observing the patient's response to stories. A patient may be told about a man who jumps from the top of the Empire State building, lands on the sidewalk, gets to his feet and walks away. If the patient says, "That's ridiculous, he should be dead," the psychiatrist knows that his judgment is sound. Or he may ask the patient what he would do if he found a stamped, addressed and sealed envelope on the pavement. When appearance, behavior, mood, speech, thinking, memory, intelligence, orientation and judgment are combined, the result is the mental status of the patient, which is as important in psychiatry as is the result of physical examination in medicine. A mental status is in large part the basis of psychiatric diagnosis.

A diagnosing psychiatrist must also deal with the entities of psychiatric diseases. The classification of mental diseases was recently revised and published by the American Psychiatric Association. This new classification is used throughout this book, but the orders are not identical.

The new diagnostic nomenclature lists mental retardation and organic brain syndromes at the head of the list of mental disorders. Mental retardation is characterized by a low intelligence and is usually evident shortly after the individual is born. The organic brain syndromes, on the other hand, include illnesses that can develop at any age. In the organic brain syndromes, the brain is organically disturbed by tumors, infection, trauma, degenerative diseases, etc. The typical result is a disturbance in orientation, memory, intelligence, and judgment. Mental retardation and the organic brain syndromes are considered together in Chapter 7.

The new nomenclature then lists the psychoses not attrib-

	Schizophrenia Odd	Manic + (plus)	Depressed - (minus)	Acute Organic Fearful, disoriented	Chronic Organic Released	Neurosis Complaints	Personality Disorders Acting out
Appearance	Odd	+	-	Fearful	Released	Complaints	O. K. (1)
Behavior or Activity	Odd	+ (overactive ↔ furor)	- (underactive ↔ stupor)	Fearful	Released	Complaints (compulsions, conversion symptoms)	O. K.
Mood or Affect	Odd (inappropriate)	+ (hostility underneath happiness)	- (sad, depressed)	Fearful	Released (emotional lability)	Complaints (depressed, anxious)	O. K.
Speech	Odd (disassociation)	+ (overtalkative ↔ push of speech)	- (undertalkative ↔ mute)	Fearful, confused (tremulous)	Released (dysarthria)	Complaints (stammering)	O. K.
Thinking or Mental Content	Odd (delusions, hallucinations)	+	-	Fearful, confused ± vivid, perceived hallucinations	Released	Complaints (obsessions, compulsions, phobias, physical symptoms)	O. K.
Memory	±	±	±	± (confused)	Released (lives in past, loss of recent memory)	O. K. (Amnesia)	O. K.
Intelligence	±	±	±	±	±	O. K. (learning blocks)	O. K.
Orientation	±	±	±	Disoriented	±	O. K.	O. K.
Judgment	±	±	±	±	±	O. K.	O. K.

*This diagnostic "sheet," used in teaching third-year psychiatry at Harvard Medical School, is reprinted with permission of Dr. Elvin V. Semrad.
(1) Mental status normal —diagnosis made on basis of history of acting out.
O.K. = normal or not involved.
± = may or may not be involved.
+ = increased.
∓ = usually involved, but need not be.
- = decreased.

utable to physical conditions. These are the so-called *functional* psychoses of schizophrenia, affective psychoses, paranoid states, etc. In *schizophrenia,* contact with reality is disturbed, and patients think bizarre thoughts and live in a world that is not that of other people. Schizophrenia is treated in Chapters 5 and 6. The *affective psychoses* include illnesses in which the affect or mood is primarily involved, and Chapter 8 is devoted to this type of mental illness. The *neuroses* are those illnesses which are characterized by the presence of anxiety. Neurotic patients complain of uncomfortable feelings of anxiety or of the disguised forms that anxiety can take. The neuroses are presented in Chapter 11. A special form of neurosis, namely, the depressive neurosis or reactive depression, is reserved for a chapter of its own (Chapter 9).

The *personality disorders* are characterized by acting out that gives rise to abnormal behavior patterns. These abnormal behavioral patterns are described in Chapter 10. However, this category also includes sexual deviation (Chapter 11), alcoholism (Chapter 7), and drug dependence (Chapter 7). The diagnosis of personality disorder is usually made on the basis of the history, and many of these patients exhibit no abnormalities of mental status.

The nomenclature then lists the various *psychophysiological disorders.* This category of illness is characterized by complaints of physical symptoms which are caused by emotional factors. These illnesses are considered in Chapter 11.

A diagnosing psychiatrist may have to diagnose special symptoms, transient situational disturbances, and conditions without manifest psychiatric disorder, such as marital maladjustment. Such conditions are considered throughout this book, but no separate chapter has been devoted to them.

The chart on page 8 is a convenient summary of the diagnostic categories in terms of the changes that can be observed in the mental status. While the diagnosis of mental disorders can usually be made from the mental status examination, most psychiatrists feel it is just as important to understand *how* and *why* the illness developed. It is for this reason that the patient's history has become a necessary tool in psychiatric diagnostic procedures. In physical medicine, surgery, obstetrics, or ophthalmology a history is automatically taken of every patient admitted to a ward. It varies according to the diligence of the doctor doing the work-up; when the patient is in shock or great pain, there is, of course, no time to record a detailed history as other measures must be immediately undertaken. Medical histories are therefore sometimes very brief, while psychiatric histories are usually very long; they are, indeed, so involved and lengthy that they are referred to by a special term, *anamnesis,* which means recalling of things past.

The first thing to know in an anamnesis is the *informant* who tells the patient's story, for it might be his wife who hates him and slants her story accordingly, or his mother whose love controls her version of events, or the patient himself who may not be entirely reliable. To know the source of all material helps the psychiatrist assess its validity.

The psychiatrist then wants to know the *reason for admission* to the hospital. The patient may have come in by himself because he was so depressed that he could no longer go on living that way; indeed, he may have attempted suicide. Another patient's actions were so anti-social that he got involved in robbery, rape, murder or some other crime, and the judge at his trial may have concluded that he should be placed under observation. Psychiatrists want to know whether the patient has grown increasingly confused, has had peculiar thoughts and feelings or difficulty in concentrating. Perhaps his family decided that he needed help. In short, what are the exact reasons for his being in the psychiatric ward? Some of the answers are astounding.

The third essential component of an anamnesis is the *patient's past history,* beginning preferably before birth, so that the first category here is "birth and development." His mother's pregnancy is important; there may have been a marked effect upon him if she had to get married and he was born soon after, or if her pregnancy developed only after years of married life. Such information helps the psychiatrist familiarize himself with the patient's problems. It is significant whether he was a first or tenth child, whether his birth was normal or so difficult that his mother could have no more children and so grew to resent him. Then, there are the patient's feelings and behavior as a baby. It is helpful to know whether he bit his mother's breast or took it readily, whether he changed easily to a bottle, whether he had a habit of holding food in his mouth, refusing to swallow, and whether he changed to semi-solid food without much difficulty. After changing to solid food, babies must learn to control their bowels. How did the patient's family handle this problem—were they strict or lenient? Such material in the category of birth and development helps shape psychiatric understanding and diagnosis of illness.

Next comes a group of pre-school factors, occurring up to the age of six or seven. It is helpful to know whether the patient was then a behavior problem: antagonistic, resistive, with frequent temper tantrums. His school record, the next item, tells not only how far he went in school but also how he got along there. Was he the teacher's pet or the class' bad boy, a dunce or an excellent student? Typically, he may have been the bright student without a friend, or the most sociable boy in his class with many friends but no success at all in his work. Also significant is the patient's occupational history after he has finished school. For example, he may have done work that was not legitimate. His pay or salary, through the years, may have been going up or down. What were his relationships with his boss, his co-workers, his employees? Sexual history is included. Education in sex may have been given by the patient's family or picked up on the street. In the case of a girl, data on menstruation is enlightening, while for a boy "wet dreams" are significant; in both sexes it is important to know about masturbation. Marital happiness should be described in terms of the sexual and psychological adjustment, the children's adjustment, etc. Social history must also be recorded—whether the patient is a respected member of his community or has been in trouble with the police; whether religion or politics are a source of trouble and anxiety for him; in other words, whether he experiments with crackpot sects and parties.

Fourthly, psychiatrists are very thorough in unearthing the *family history*, for they have a cherished concept that personality rests at any given time on what has gone before; that a person today is the sum of what has happened to him in the past and is understandable only in that light. Since nothing forms a greater part of anyone's past than his family, it is extremely important in an anamnesis. Family history includes the usual medical work-up—history of cancer, tuberculosis, rheumatism, arthritis, etc.—but goes on to descriptions of personalities in the family as far back as the two sets of grandparents, for even they have a great effect on growing children. It involves parents and siblings, the latter being a technical term for "brothers and sisters," used because it is easy to write and to say. In addition, psychiatrists are interested in knowing how all these individuals got along in society. The patient's mother may have been a prostitute or his father an alcoholic, or everyone in the family may have been in a reformatory at one time or another. Since religion is important in its effect on a patient, it is necessary to know whether his family is devout, has changed faith, and whether there were any divorces, remarriages and separations. The examining psychiatrist has now arrived at one of the main

---

[1] Harry Stack Sullivan was born in 1892 and died in 1949. He powerfully stimulated American psychiatry by developing the theme of interpersonal relationships. He coined the term *parataxic distortion,* one of his many useful contributions. Parataxic distortion or parataxic illusion means the distortion of subsequent opportunities for personal growth by earlier anxiety experiences, and he emphasized the effects of these parataxic distortions in

points of interest according to Harry Stack Sullivan,[1] namely the interpersonal relationships in the patient's family. To find out exactly what went on in the patient's relationships with his mother, father, siblings and grandparents is a difficult task, indeed. The psychiatrist also needs to get all possible data on mental illnesses in the family. Some diseases seem hereditary, making it easier to diagnose a mental illness afflicting grandmother, mother and daughter, when the last happens to be the patient. Furthermore, mental illness has a very important effect on all family relationships. People are not ashamed of an appendectomy, fractured spine, gallbladder operation, or heart failure, for these are "respectable" ailments; but they are ashamed of mental illness. They may refuse to say that their mother is in the State Hospital, or that they themselves are seeing a psychiatrist regularly. Everything suddenly becomes secret. There is no doubt that mental illness affects a patient's family differently from physical illness.

The fifth and final factor in a personal history is the *story of the present illness.* Its seeds are usually to be found in early childhood as far back as the age of three or four; ultimate admission to the hospital may thus occur after a considerable period of time. Sometimes, however, the origin of the illness is only two or three years distant. In searching for a precipitating event from which to date the history of the present illness, psychiatrists find such causes as overwork, marital tensions, religious problems, and job difficulties— whatever seems to make the illness obvious. A careful description of how the illness developed is then required. A patient may have experienced mild depression at first which became

---

hindering mutual understanding in interpersonal relationships. He founded his own school of psychiatric thinking with its own methods of therapy, with many adherents, and the publication of its own journal. He, along with Karen Horney, is considered a "neo-Freudian" in that he tries to combine the individually-oriented psychoanalysis of Freud with the concept of the individual in his interpersonal relationships with other individuals.

progressively worse and ended in an attempt at suicide; or a student may seek help because he finds his work harder and harder, cannot concentrate as well as before, and has begun to hear frightening voices.

When all the information relating to the two categories of anamnesis and mental status has been assembled, it is possible to make a diagnosis conforming to one of the several categories of mental disorder: mental retardation, organic, schizophrenic, affective, neurotic, or personality disorder. In diagnosing, psychiatrists use a deductive process similar to that employed in diagnosing physical ailments.

More important than diagnosis are the dynamics of the patient's illness, for psychiatrists today are interested not merely in *what* came about, but also in *why*. Why did the patient suddenly start to hear voices or become depressed? Why did he try to kill himself? The modern psychiatric orientation is *dynamic* in that it aims at more than labelling a patient as manic, schizophrenic, etc. Psychiatrists try to understand and to explain illness in the conviction that on that basis they are far more able to give their patients the effective help so desperately needed in all cases.

RECOMMENDED READING

For complete bibliographic data, see also the General Bibliography following the Preface.

Batchelor: *Henderson and Gillespie's Textbook of Psychiatry for Students and Practitioners,* chapters 3 and 5.

Cobb, S. *Borderlands of Psychiatry.* Cambridge: Harvard University Press, 1943.

Ewalt and Farnsworth: *Textbook of Psychiatry,* chapter 5.

Kolb: *Noyes' Modern Clinical Psychiatry,* chapter 8.

Menninger, K. *A Manual for Psychiatric Case Study,* Second edition. New York: Grune & Stratton, 1962.

Sullivan, H. S. *The Psychiatric Interview.* New York: W. W. Norton and Co., 1954.

Whitehorn, J. "Guide to Interviewing and Clinical Personality Study." *Archives of Neurology & Psychiatry,* 1944, 52:197-216.

PART II

Development of the Normal Personality

CHAPTER 2

Psychosexual Development

In a consideration of the development of human personality, three major kinds of factors emerge: the constitutional, the developmental, and the situational. In the first group are placed the elements of personality that are hereditary or congenital; developmental factors occur in the process of growing up; and there are other factors called situational because they come from situations arising in the individual's environment.

The *constitutional factors* existing at birth represent a substratum upon which the rest of a personality is built; there are several constitutional factors. One of them is known as *body build* or habitus. Although many people have studied this field, Kretschmer[1] was mainly responsible for the division of people into three groups on the basis of body builds. After examining both normal and abnormal people,

---

[1] Ernst Kretschmer was born in 1888. In 1927, he advanced the claim that by determining certain indices of a person's bodily dimensions one can assign him to a certain physical type, and then safely conclude therefrom his general temperamental makeup. Although he made other contributions to the field of psychiatry, he is best known for this work on somatotypes.

17

he then classified them as *pyknics,* those who are short and fat, *asthenics,* who are tall and thin, and *athletics,* who are muscular. A certain correlation was detected between the body types and mental illness: pyknics tended toward affective illnesses, asthenics toward schizophrenia, and athletics toward neuroses.

Version is another important factor, elaborated for the most part by the famous psychiatrist, Jung.[2] Version expresses the idea that emotions can be directed in several ways, the term itself coming from a Latin word meaning a direction or a turning. Jung found that people could be extroverted, introverted or ambiverted. Extroverts are those whose emotions are turned outward into the external world, the life-of-the-party types who do not think very much about themselves; introverts have their emotional streams directed inwards, so that they think about themselves a great deal, and are often the thinkers of society; while ambiverts are a fairly equal mixture of extroversion and introversion. Further study of such factors suggested that the pyknic tends to be an extrovert and to have an affective illness if he takes sick; the asthenic inclines toward introversion and toward schizophrenia if ill; and people who are athletic in body build are usually ambiverted and tend to become neurotic if they become ill.

A third constitutional factor are the *congenital ano-*

---

[2] Carl Gustav Jung, a brilliant and profound psychiatrist, was born in 1875. Around 1906, while an assistant to Eugen Bleuler, he became interested in the phenomenon of emotional version. In 1908, he joined Sigmund Freud and assisted in forming the International Psychoanalytic Association. While connected with Freud, he made many basic contributions to the understanding of the mental association processes and the influences of emotional feelings on word associations (the precursor of the lie detector). In 1911, he left psychoanalysis and severed his relationship with Freud. Apparently, this break occurred because Jung was unable to follow the purely biological views of Freud and the examination of the sexual phenomena involved. After this separation, Jung founded his own school of therapy, based on the concept of the *collective unconscious* (an inherited, innate aspect of personality common to all individuals).

malies with which everyone is familiar, such defects present at birth as club foot, harelip, crossed eyes, etc. They are included in a consideration of the development of personality because the body partly determines the way people meet the external world. People react to each other partly in accordance with external appearances; any congenital anomaly influences personality. A fourth factor is intellectual ability. This is present at birth, is measured by different tests, and is usually expressed in terms of an I.Q. (Intelligence Quotient). Constitutional factors are not being discussed in detail here, mainly because they are difficult to influence and because little can be done about them. For the most part they simply exist for better or for worse.

The second group of factors, called *developmental,* will be given a more detailed treatment because a great deal is known about them and because they are subject to change. It will be recalled that these factors occur as an individual grows up. They are of several kinds: first, a category referred to as *libido* or *psychosexual development.* Since there is no field of medicine, perhaps no discipline in the world, of which people form more misconceptions than of psychiatry, all terms used must be carefully defined. Libido, by definition, means *psychic energy.* It could be compared to electricity flowing through a high-tension wire; or one might say that it is a little like the basal metabolic rate, the body's energy exchange. Libido, the energy behind psychic processes, finds outward expression through psychological needs. Just as the turn of a switch sends electricity through a wire to light a lamp, so the libido finds expression in terms of needs, the gratification of which is known as *psychosexual activity.* For example, psychic energy might express itself as an itch, a need to scratch, and when the individual has gratified this need by scratching he has performed a psychosexual activity. Another example lies in the impact of psychic energy or libido on the stomach, causing·hunger;

again, when food is taken and hunger appeased a psycho-sexual activity is completed. Many persons who read Freud[3] or other psychiatrists might exclaim with disgust, "But this is all sex!" A more careful appraisal would show them that they have failed to take into account the psychiatric definition of sex as merely the gratification of a need. Clearly, this definition differs greatly from ordinary usage in which the word applies only to dating, necking, marriage, intercourse, etc. These activities are also included in the psychiatric definition of sex because they, like eating, sleeping, scratching, etc., do satisfy needs. To repeat these important definitions, libido means psychic energy, while psychosexual activity means the gratification of any need.

Libido centers in various areas of the body as life progresses, so that psychosexual activities take place predominantly in those areas. A chronology of approximate ages can be established for the stages of libidinal development. The first period of psychosexual development, the *oral stage,* extends through the first year of life. It is characterized by various activities of the mouth—oral activities—such as crying, vomiting, sucking, chewing and eating, all of which involve the lips, mouth and the upper end of the gastrointestinal tract. The baby's libido, centered in the oral area, expresses itself as an overwhelming need for food. When this demand is satisfied by eating, a psychosexual activity is performed.

[3] Sigmund Freud was born on May 6, 1856, and died on September 23, 1939. The most famous figure in the field of psychiatry, he was the founder of psychoanalysis, a method of exploring the unconscious for research purposes and of making it conscious for therapeutic purposes. Among his many original contributions were his libido theory, the theory of the id, ego, and superego, the theory of the conscious and the unconscious, the theory of transference, and the theory of dream interpretation. He has been followed by many disciples who have founded schools of Freudian psychoanalysis throughout this country and Europe, and by many part- or non-believers who have founded deviant schools of their own.

Near the end of the first year of life a second stage is reached, the *anal stage*, which lasts roughly for another year. Here bowel training becomes the infant's major concern. There are several possible reasons why human beings do not remain at the oral stage all of their lives. First, parental pressure causes them to change, for mothers do not mind feeding their babies but strongly wish to train them to control their bowels so as to be rid of the nuisance of changing and washing diapers. A second reason for the change to the anal stage is social pressure. In communities where there are many young mothers, a sort of mysterious competition takes place in which the highest honors go to the first to teach her baby successful bowel control. A third reason is of a physiological nature. The motor fibers which connect the central nervous system with the anal sphincter allow for voluntary control of the sphincter by the motor or precentral cortex; these fibers, however, do not begin to work until the end of the first year of life. Just as a baby cannot walk at birth, so is he incontinent of feces—in fact, he is in this respect quite like the victim of a cerebrovascular accident. One might well wonder how the gratification of libido is involved in bowel training. The answer is that in the anal stage the need for love and approval continues to exist, but is centered on the process of controlling the bowels. An infant is placed on the toilet and urged to move his bowels by promises that his mother will love him all the more. She may say encouragingly: "Do this for me and you'll be my darling baby." Furthermore, she adds a prohibition of bowel movements made in any other place than on the toilet. Thus, when the child has succeeded in learning control and has been kissed and praised by his mother and family and neighbors, his need for love and approval has been gratified and a psychosexual activity performed. It might be emphasized here that pleasure is to be gained from accepting restrictions and by getting along within the bounds of social propriety.

The third stage in human development, the *genital* stage,* extends roughly from the second to the sixth year of life. There are two possible reasons for the change from the anal to the genital stage. Physiologically speaking, the sensory fibers from the genital organs to the central nervous system do not begin to function until the end of the second year, when sensations can begin to travel from the genitals to the brain where they are appreciated in the sensory postcentral cortex. There is an evident proof of this development in the fact that babies can be circumcised shortly after birth without pain. A second reason may be parental in nature, namely, the attention to the child's genitals in bathing and powdering. The attention to the genitals and the ability of the child to perceive the sensations as pleasant coalesce, the need for pleasure is gratified, and again a psychosexual activity has been performed.

Two new factors emerge during the genital stage: the Oedipus complex, which is so important that it will be reserved for a separate chapter, and *infantile masturbation*. Several remarks can be made about the latter phenomenon: it is universal, unconscious, diffuse and wholly harmless. Infantile masturbation is universal; parents can observe it in every child, if they are willing to see it. Scientific studies have proved conclusively that during the period from two to six every infant at some time indulges in masturbation. It is unconscious because the child is not aware of what he is doing, for the act is wholly involuntary, an automatic activity. It is diffuse in that it is not specifically directed at any part of the body. A boy may rub his hand over the general area of his genitals, while a girl may rub her thighs together, the activity in either case being no more specific than the

---

* Most books do not distinguish between the genital and phallic stages, but the author finds this method of presentation easier and more logical.

diffuse motion. It is important to realize also that infantile masturbation is harmless, old wives' tales notwithstanding.

A fourth period in the development of the libido is called the *latency stage* and extends roughly from the sixth to the thirteenth year. There are many possible reasons for the change from the genital to the latency stage. First of all, by the time a child has reached the end of his genital stage, he really is in need of a time for rest, recuperation and consolidation. This is because of the tremendous effort required to meet the challenge of the oral and anal stages, and to surmount the great hurdle of the Oedipus complex. He had to learn that food is not the most important thing in life; he then had to accept and comply with the demands of society as symbolized in the process of bowel training; and in the genital period he had to contend with his parent's dislike of infantile masturbation and find the correct solution to the Oedipus complex. A second reason for the latency stage lies in the physiological or, more properly, endocrinological changes in his body. Studies of weight curves show that the birth weight doubles in the first six months of life, that during the first year of life a baby triples his birth weight, and that the child's growth curve gradually slows down until the age of six years when it seems to level off until the age of puberty. Around the thirteenth year the endocrine glands become active once more, and faster growth begins anew. Since these glands are quiet during the growth plateau from six to thirteen, the child's psyche also is quiescent and latent. To define the latency period in terms of psychosexual activity is obviously rather difficult as there is little visible need of gratification involved; there is, however, the undisputed need of the child for quiescence and peace, and gratification of this need will serve to qualify the interval as a psychosexual process. Some writers stress the fact of change from internal to external concerns so that social strivings and power struggles become important needs during this age period. The gratification of the need for belonging and acceptance in social groups can be seen as a psychosexual act.

Fifth comes the *phallic* or *clitoral stage,* beginning about the thirteenth year when the individual is adolescent. The terms phallic and clitoral demand explanation. Phallos is the Greek word for penis. The latinized form deriving from it is phallus which means image of the penis, a symbol of it. In many cultures and religious systems the phallus was venerated, carried around in processions, notably at the festivals of Dionysus. Throughout history, strange beliefs, superstitions, fears, and taboos surrounded sex and sexual intercourse, particularly intercourse with a virgin. To commit the act of defloration was thought to bring horrible consequences upon the man. In order to solve this dilemma, the idol of a god had to take over. Wedding ceremonies in many districts of India and in Rome (according to early Christian writers) required the bride to seat herself on the phallus of the statue; this took away her virginity and shifted the penalty for so doing to the god. When the term phallic was introduced into psychiatry it was a synonym for the word penile which in medical usage had been more or less appropriated by dermatologists and syphilologists. To refer to a penile stage of psychosexual development would have sounded quite ridiculous—as if having syphilis were a normal period of development. No such trouble could be expected from using the term clitoral stage when referring to the psychosexual development of girls. Although the clitoris remains an imperfectly developed organ (a vestigial organ), clitoral stage is on a par with phallic stage in psychiatric usage because the clitoris and the penis have the same embryological origin.

The main reason for the change to this stage lies, as has been mentioned, in physiological factors. The endocrinologically dictated changes of puberty occur. A boy begins to grow a beard and body hair, his voice changes, and he begins to experience nocturnal emissions or wet dreams, as they are called. These begin to occur early in puberty when his sexual glands become operative and make him capable of the same kind of ejaculations he will later have in marital intercourse. The emissions usually occur at night—hence the term nocturnal—and are associated with a pleasant dream, often sexual in nature. At this age the dream is not truly of a genital type involving intercourse, but may represent a date, touching a girl's hand or seeing her smile. On awaking the boy discovers that he has had an emission of seminal fluid. The phenomenon is completely normal and almost universal in boys entering puberty. Girls, at this stage, begin to develop breasts, body hair and "figures," and begin to menstruate—all evidences of puberty. It is important that thirteen years be taken as an approximate age for puberty; some girls, for example, begin to menstruate at nine or ten, others at sixteen or seventeen, and still others as late as eighteen or twenty.

During the phallic or clitoral stage, about the age of thirteen, adolescent masturbation begins. This act is almost universal, conscious, specific and harmless. The qualification *almost* is added to universal because adolescents, unlike babies, cannot be observed with complete objectivity: they are in school, out on dates, parties, etc.; parents are unreliable informants on the subject, while some adolescents will admit masturbation and some won't. Secondly, some adolescents are so busy growing up in terms of going to school, studying, sports, dating, etc., that they never get around to masturbating, making it just as normal not to masturbate as to do so. Adolescent masturbation is described as conscious because the individual is aware of what he is doing; it is a voluntary act involving free will. Such masturbation is specific, no longer the vague and diffuse rubbing of infantile masturbation; a boy takes his penis in his hand

and gives it a to-and-fro motion until he produces an ejaculation, while a girl manipulates her clitoris with her finger, face-cloth, powder-puff, pillow, etc., and may bring herself to an orgasm or sexual climax. Adolescent masturbation is wholly harmless, the tales of physical and mental damage from it being nonsensical and purely imaginary.

In women, theoretically at least, there is a sixth stage of libidinal or psychosexual development. It is usually stated in psychological treatises that women have a more difficult time than men. Perhaps the fact that most psychiatrists are men explains that their literature is slanted so that women seem to suffer a little more. In any case, men are all set when they reach the phallic stage, but women still have farther to go. *Vaginal* is the term applied to their sixth stage of psychosexual development. It comes into being with the first sexual intercourse. No definite age can thus be assigned to this stage, as some women have intercourse before menstruation, some after marriage, and some never. With the first intercourse a normal woman's process of need and subsequent gratification, formerly centered on the clitoris, becomes focused in the vagina. In intercourse very little attention is paid to the clitoris, for the penis is inserted in the vagina and it is there that the frictions occur.

It is enlightening to consider some of the difficulties that individuals encounter in passing through this developmental schema. During the oral stage, difficulty comes in parental attitudes. Everyone is familiar with the two types of mothers who represent the extremes of harmful conduct, the "too much" and the "too little" mothers. The first feels that she has to force every drop of milk or spoonful of food into her baby's mouth. It makes no difference to her whether he wants only two spoonfuls of food, she forces him to swallow four; if his bottle holds four ounces of milk, he is never permitted to take only three. Such forced feeding leads to an oral excess against which the child may rebel, becoming extremely negatively disposed towards all oral activity. This kind of child may develop into a finicky and fussy eater, a stingy and tight-mouthed adult. The second type of maternal error is represented by the "too little" mother. If her baby wakes up hungry before the time specified in her book of instructions, she refuses to feed him; if he finishes his bottle and wants some more, she leaves him unsatisfied. Such a regimen leaves the child orally deprived, so that he grows up feeling that something is missing which should have been there in his childhood; he may compensate as an adult by over-indulgence in oral activity of all kinds, by talking, drinking, eating, smoking, chewing, etc. It is interesting to note that alcoholics fall into this category of orally deprived persons.

During the anal stage difficulty is encountered when bowel training has been carried out either too strictly or too leniently. By too strictly is meant that it was too harshly carried through, that too much fuss was made about it, or that it was begun too early. It has already been pointed out that the motor fibers from the central nervous system to the anal sphincter do not begin to function until the end of the first year of life. Imagine, then, a mother putting her baby on the toilet seat before he has conscious control of his anal sphincter. The result of such attempts at bowel training may set up a behavior pattern of trying and failing, for though the child wants to be loved and to have the approval of society, he is physically unable to comply with his mother's demands. Such a person frequently grows up with a feeling that success in any activity is impossible for him to achieve.

Too lenient bowel training usually occurs when parents have read a book on child development which they have misinterpreted. They feel that they have learned the dangers of being too strict and decide not to give their child any bowel training at all. Since such a child feels that he can move his bowels wherever he wishes without fear of reproof, he grows up with the conviction that he can do whatever he desires, that society has set no limits on his wishes. Consequent loss of respect for society may produce an individual unconsciously convinced that he may rob, kill and commit other crimes when he feels like it.

The major difficulty of the genital stage is parental attitudes towards infantile masturbation. It is important for a child to feel that his genitals are just as good as his hands, feet, mouth, or any other part of his body; he should feel that it is as right to play with his penis as to indulge in some other childish activity. When parents sharply prohibit touching or playing with genitals, they make the child feel that all genital activity is wrong and forbidden. Yet, parents expect their children to marry and to enjoy the sexual aspects of marriage. Thus, parents should remember that infantile masturbation is quite normal. The other great problem of this period, the solution of the Oedipus complex, is discussed in the following chapter.

During the latency stage, covering a child's years in grammar school, from about the age of six to thirteen, the major threat is that quiescence may be disturbed. In this age period, rape and homosexual seduction are most frequent; indeed, the newspapers are full of stories about the rape of eight-year-old girls and the introduction of young boys into homosexual activity. Some people who have been seduced during the latency stage have difficulty later on in life because they develop feelings adverse to marriage and other adult relationships; most people, however, who have been seduced seem to recover from the experience with no ill effects.

During the phallic or clitoral stage there may be fresh danger from parents. A boy's mother may scold him and take a generally harsh attitude towards his nocturnal emissions, which are a perfectly normal and inevitable occurrence; on the other hand, she can be understanding and explain what is happening, thereby assuaging some of the very real fears boys have when wet dreams first occur. Similarly, a girl's first menstruation should be handled sympathetically and realistically by her mother, for the picture she paints of this normal physical development will have a very important effect on her daughter's feelings about being a woman.

These examples of the dangers inherent in the developmental stages have been somewhat exaggerated for the purposes of clarity and emphasis, but in no case has anything rare or unusual been depicted.

RECOMMENDED READING

For complete bibliographic data, see also the General Bibliography following the Preface.

Abraham: *Selected Papers,* pp. 248-279, 370-392, 407-417.
English and Pearson: *Common Neuroses of Children and Adults,* chapter 2.
English and Pearson: *Emotional Problems of Living,* chapters 1, 3, 5, 7, 10.
Erikson, E. H. *Childhood and Society,* Second edition. New York: W. W. Norton, 1963, chapters 2 and 7.
Fenichel: *Psychoanalytic Theory of Neurosis,* chapter 5.
Freud: Three Contributions to the Theory of Sex. *The Standard Edition,* Volume 7, pp. 125-244.
Hendrick: *Facts and Theories of Psychoanalysis,* chapters 5, 6, 7.
Silverberg, W. V. *Childhood Experience and Personal Destiny.* New York: Springer, 1952.

CHAPTER 3

Solution of the Oedipus Complex

The development of libido, the psychosexual component in human personality, has been discussed in the previous chapter; we shall now consider a second developmental factor, the Oedipus complex, which normally evolves between the ages of four and six. In order to grasp this factor it is necessary to understand two psychiatric concepts involving four terms: namely, love and hate, and homosexual and heterosexual relationships. *Love* and *hate* are used in psychiatry as a sort of shorthand terminology to express positive and negative feelings, respectively. Thus by "love" is implied the whole range of positive emotions, from merely liking someone to deep friendship, love, marriage, etc. Similarly, "hate" in psychiatric terms means all negative feelings, from simple dislike to the desire to kill. By using this language, psychiatrists are freed from the necessity of constantly stating the specific positive or negative emotion involved in a case. In a psychiatric context they may say that a boy loves his mother but do not necessarily mean that he has sexual feelings towards her. To say that he hates his father does not specifically mean he wishes to kill him, but includes all negative emotions, of which the desire to kill may or may not be one. The second concept involves the terms *homosexual* and *heterosexual* both of which are fast becoming a part of ordinary speech in America. Psychiatrically speaking, homosexual applies to *any* relationship between two individuals of the same sex; it does not have the specifically sexual implication as in ordinary usage, although psychiatrists, of course, use it also in that context. The inclusive psychiatric usage of the term is justified by many years of psychiatric practice. For example, a friendship of a man and his male neighbor, or a luncheon date between two women is homosexual in the psychiatric meaning of the word. The two friends do not kiss or go to bed together, but the fact that both are of the same sex makes their relationship homosexual. In like fashion, heterosexual applies to any relationship between two persons of opposite sex, to a secretary's admiration of her male employer, for instance, or to a nurse's liking of a doctor, and does not necessarily signify any physical relationship between them. Such relationships are heterosexual just as are those between a man and his wife or between a pair of young lovers.

Armed with an understanding of the concepts of love and hate, and homosexuality and heterosexuality, it is possible to approach the Oedipus concept with a minimum of difficulty and misconception.

The *story* of Oedipus from which the concept derives is that of a young man who killed his father and married his mother. The circumstances which made Oedipus commit the double crime are told in the legend of Oedipus and the *Oedipus Rex* of Sophocles. Laius, king of Thebes, did not want his wife, Jocasta, to have a child because the Delphic oracle had warned him that the child would murder him. But Laius got drunk and begot a child. Immediately after Jocasta bore a son, he took him away from her, drove a nail through his feet, and carried him off to the mountains where he left him to die. The child, however, was found by the neighboring Corinthians, was named Oedipus (swollen foot), and adopted by the childless king and queen of Corinth.

Oedipus grew up to manhood, loving the king and queen whom he thought to be his real parents. One day, on a visit to Delphi, he asked the Delphic oracle about his future. When he learned of the crimes he was to commit—killing his father and marrying his mother—he left Corinth in great horror, resolving never to return. On a narrow road leading away from the city, a fancy carriage ran over his foot and virtually pushed him off the road. In an outburst of rage he killed the driver and flung the passenger on the road, who, caught in the reins, was killed by the frightened horses. The passenger was Laius, his father; but Oedipus did not know this.

As Oedipus approached Thebes he came upon the Sphinx. The Sphinx was a monster perched on a mountain who terrorized the townspeople of Thebes by asking all passers-by "the riddle of the Sphinx" and devouring them if they could not answer. Oedipus, however, solved the riddle, whereupon the Sphinx killed herself by leaping from the mountain, and the grateful Thebans made him their king. He married the queen, not knowing that she was his mother, Jocasta, and reigned happily and peacefully for many years. They had four children, two sons and two daughters.

When the people of Thebes were later ravaged by disease, they consulted the Delphic oracle for help. Together with an old blind seer the oracle finally told the true story of how Oedipus had killed his father and married his mother, indicating that the plague would stop when Laius' murderer was driven from the country. On learning the truth, Jocasta hung herself and Oedipus blinded himself. Oedipus then went into exile and wandered through the Greek countries until the furies caught up with him and chased him to his death.

In the developmental schema as it has been previously outlined, everything is pretty much the same for both boys and girls during the oral and anal periods; this ceases to be true with the advent of the genital stage at which the Oedipus complex makes its appearance. Since here again the process is simpler for the male than the female, a boy's Oedipus complex will be taken up first. His mother or a substitute in the form of a nurse is the first person with whom a boy has a sustained contact after birth. In the oral stage she feeds him; in his anal period it is to gain her love and respect that he learns to control his bowel movements. It is a positive emotional relationship—a love relationship in psychiatric terms—and it is heterosexual.

The boy's feelings towards his mother are intensely positive at this stage. During the preschool period, the little four-year old stays home all day, enjoying an extremely close and pleasant love relationship with his mother. Up to the age of four or five he was fed and tucked away in bed before his father came home, so that he did not see much of him. Now he stays up until seven or eight o'clock and begins to come into real contact with this person who goes out to work and provides the money to support the home. Thus it is that his father begins to make a real appearance in his emotional life. Since the boy's messy, noisy habits disturb his parents' enjoyment of a quiet mealtime together, he is told to "run along and play;" for the first time in his life he is definitely in the way. When his father is at home, the boy's intensely positive love relationship with his mother is disturbed, even destroyed, and he soon develops a strong negative feeling towards the intruder, a feeling of real hatred. This becomes even more pronounced when he realizes that, at bedtime, his mother and father invariably go to bed together, while he has to sleep all alone. He feels lost and isolated with no one to comfort him, especially since he knows that his mother has his father with her; indeed, he begins to wonder why his father had to make an appearance in the first place. The biblical "lex talionis"— the law which says, "an eye for an eye, a tooth for a tooth"—

is the principle by which children reason at the age of four or five. The boy is only too aware of his negative, hateful, even murderous feelings towards his father and of the fact that he would like the father to die so that he, the son, could have his mother all to himself once more. Reasoning in this way, he assumes his father feels exactly the same about him, finding the son a hated intruder into his own relationship with his wife. More complications are in store, because when a boy is in the genital stage all his libido, all his psychosexual energy is focussed on his penis. The boy's distress, very real and violent, becomes centered, therefore, in his feelings about his penis, the most important organ during the genital stage; eventually he comes to believe that his father dislikes his, the son's, penis just as he, the son, would like to cut off the father's. What develops in the boy is the so-called *castration complex,* a two-edged sword, for the intensity with which the boy wishes that his father did not have a penis determines exactly the intensity of the hatred he assumes the latter feels toward his penis. The conflict raging back and forth in his mind leaves him in a truly unhappy situation at this stage of development.

The confused and difficult period that has just been described is the original Oedipal situation. The boy is now at the age of four or five, wishing his father would work all the time and never come home again but knowing full well that his father supports the home and has a perfect right to eat and sleep there. The boy wants desperately to sleep with his mother, but she invariably goes to bed with his father and leaves him all alone. His rosy, warm and pleasant world of exclusive love with his mother has collapsed. Frustrations unknown before now arise from the need to renounce desires; merely moving his bowels on the toilet does no longer suffice to earn him love and approval. To this unpleasant state of affairs there is, happily, a successful normal solution, or resolution.

In solving the Oedipus complex, hate feelings are taken care of first, as they are the more troublesome. The psychiatric principle which states that it is easier to love than to hate will be borne out by reflecting on the great amount of energy required to hate just one person while one can like a great many with no trouble at all. The solution therefore begins with the disappearance of hate towards the father. The key to this disappearance is *identification*, a process by which the boy enters into a close relationship with his father. In psychiatric parlance, identification means incorporation into oneself of another's traits, personality, and character. Everyone has experienced this process at one time or another, perhaps by incorporating the dress or hair-style of an admired friend, or the ideas and attitudes of a beloved teacher or relative. The process is thoroughly useful; in solving the Oedipus complex it works along the lines of the Graeco-Roman maxim, "If you can't beat them, join them."

Our five-year old boy in finding the normal solution to his Oedipus complex follows precisely the same logic. His reasoning at this period might be somewhat as follows: "Daddy and I are in a state of undeclared war: we both want to cut off the other's penis, we hate each other to death, he wants to be rid of me and I want to be rid of him. What is the best thing to do? Obviously, I cannot overcome him, so the best thing to do is to unite with him. I will join him and together we'll form a union of men. Then, when he and I are men together, we won't fight anymore, and everything will be wonderful." Such reasoning leads him to identify with his father, so that his terrific hostility and hatred die. The two become friends, go to baseball games, they golf or fish together, and are now like one person in their union of men. Identification with his father is the first step in the normal solution of a boy's Oedipus complex;

after that, his love relationship with his mother remains to be straightened out. In the male union with his father, he sees, there has to be fair play. Clearly, his mother is his father's woman, so it cannot be fair for him to be after her, too: two comrades cannot have the same woman. His father, he comes to understand, is the sole rightful possessor of his mother, so the boy decides to turn his own attention elsewhere, perhaps to the little girl next door. Songs have been written about this resolution of the Oedipal conflict, for instance, "I want a girl just like the girl who married dear old dad," in which there is a clear transference from the mother to an outside love object.

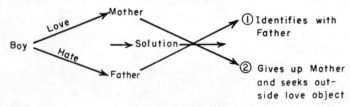

Fig. 1 Oedipus complex of the boy.

Abnormal solutions of a boy's Oedipus complex can occur for various reasons. He may never cease desiring his mother and never turn to an outside love object, in which case he will be identified with his father but unable to function as a normal male in society. He will be masculine enough, yet at forty or fifty years of age he may still be a bachelor because all his love belongs to his mother. Such men, well known in all communities, may date the most sought-after girls to no avail; they are quite unable to fall in love with them. This type of man may fixate at various other degrees of attachment to the mother. The love which holds him to her may be so complete that there is no room for another woman; it may be weakened slightly so that he can take girls out occasionally; or the bond may be weakened enough to let him propose to a girl and get married. In the last case the man is really in love with two women, his mother and his wife, producing a great deal of marital conflict, examples of which are common in psychiatric practice. Frequently, women married to such men complain of the fact that their husbands love their mothers more than their wives, which is perfectly true.

Another difficulty in the solution of the male Oedipus complex arises when the boy fails to make an identification with his father, thus never resolving the intense feelings of hatred he has built up within himself. Such a man is left for the rest of his life with hostility that erupts on the slightest provocation: he constantly shows hatred towards his employer or any superior; he cannot stand supervision or being in an inferior position, nor is he capable of taking a superior role. The abnormal solutions of a boy's Oedipus complex may be even more complicated than in the two examples just shown, for the whole process can be reversed so that the boy hates his mother, loves his father and thus identifies with his mother. The overt, active homosexuality which develops from such an erroneous identification is quite a different thing from the homosexuality previously described. By identifying with his mother the boy becomes feminine and passive, takes over the attitudes and emotions of a woman, and desires another man as a love object. It is clear, then, that the solution of the Oedipus complex is of the greatest importance in influencing the development of the individual concerned.

The Oedipus complex in girls starts from the same relationship as it does in boys: an initial, sustained contact with the mother or a mother substitute in the form of a nurse. A girl's mother feeds her during the oral stage, and it is for mother that bowel control is mastered; thus, in psychiatric terms, the girl begins life with a positive, a love relationship with her mother, which is homosexual. Because of this homosexual beginning, a girl's Oedipus complex is more complicated than the boy's which begins and ends with a heterosexual relationship. Women begin in a homosexual and must end in a heterosexual relationship. After passing through her oral and anal stages a girl begins to experience sexual curiosity at the age of four or five. During the preschool age when boys and girls get together in the attic, cellar, or behind a barn, the burning question of the moment is simply, "What have you got and what have I got?" During this universal stage of infantile sexual curiosity the children want to know why boys go into the men's room and girls into the ladies', why boys urinate standing and girls sitting, why boys wear pants and girls wear dresses, etc. Little by little a girl comes to realize through such experiences in sexual curiosity—and also by seeing her father or her brother naked—that some people have a thing called a penis which she herself does not possess. She feels deprived in much the same way she would feel if another child had a bag of candy and she had none, for in place of a penis she has only a hole. Little boys, she discovers, display their penises proudly and make her feel inferior.

So she gradually begins to feel that her mother had left something off when she brought her into the world, for she gave her brother a penis but denied one to her. As a result, the girl's feelings toward her mother change; they become what psychiatrists call *ambivalent*. There exist within the girl—all at one time—two different feelings toward her mother, love and hate. This ambivalence probably explains why women cannot make decisions so quickly as men; by nature they see both sides of every question. On the other hand, the same ambivalence accounts for that female intuition by which women are able to reach conclusions that no man, however intelligent, can attain. Hatred of her mother, then, is experienced by a girl because of *penis envy*. At this point in her development the girl, too, becomes aware of her father's presence in much the same manner as the little boy described above. She begins to stay up later in the evenings and is around when her father comes home from work at night. Feeling that her mother has cheated her by denying her a penis at birth, the girl now turns to her father in a kind of hopeful love. She knows he has a penis and hopes he may be able to supply her with one of her own. It is important to realize that the girl's love of her father is characterized by this hopeful desire to receive, whereas a boy's love is aggressive, marked by the desire to seek and to grab what he wants. Clearly, the masculine aggression and the passive feminine waiting are of prime importance in establishing the basic difference between male and female character.

However, Karen Horney[1] disputes the importance of penis envy in the Oedipus complex of the girl, and even the classical Oedipus complex really describes only the preponderant emotions in the complicated schema of interpersonal relationships in the family.

Such, then, is the girl's Oedipal situation. She would like to sleep with her father, to have a baby which might represent a penis and so put her on a level with boys. She would like her mother to stay out shopping all day long; she would

[1] Karen Horney was born in 1885. Her great contribution to psychiatry was emphasizing the cultural, social, environmental, and anthropological factors in mental illnesses. She, along with Harry Stack Sullivan, is considered a "neo-Freudian" in that she tries to combine the individually-oriented psychoanalysis of Freud with the concept of the individual in his culture and society. She deviated from Freud in seeing early childhood experiences as less important in causing neuroses than the present, actually existing, conflicts of an individual in his everyday life, and seeing the latter as existing in terms of specific cultural conditions. Many of her books are suitable for reading by interested laymen. In particular, she disputes Freud's emphasis on the importance of penis envy as a cover-up or screen for more socially and culturally determined phenomena, such as failure to live up to certain inflated culturally induced notions about the self. She founded her own school of psychiatric theory and therapy. She died in December, 1952.

even like her mother to go to the hospital and die. Her one desire is to be her father's favorite, her father's wife. While going through this period, girls are as confused and upset as boys. They have to come to the same realization that the world demands far more than successful bowel control. Life, they begin to see, means giving up desires, facing facts and conforming. Fortunately, the girl's distressing state of affairs, too, has a normal solution. First, her feelings of hatred, her ambivalence towards her mother, are straightened out by the process of identification. The girl reasons that, although her mother did not give her a penis at birth, neither does she have one herself; it is possible, therefore, to form a union of people without penises—to exclude men. As soon as she has established a firm identification with her mother, the girl's hostility disappears, and she becomes, in effect, a miniature mother. She begins to help wash the dishes, make the bed, sew, etc. She now enters into a relationship with her mother which is probably the closest and most enjoyable of all human relationships. Boys never approach this mutual understanding with their mothers; they are too aggressive and too sexually oriented. The second step in the normal solution of a girl's Oedipus complex is the straightening out of her love for her father. Again, by a process similar to that of the little boy she realizes that her father belongs to her mother, that "he's her man," and that in the union of women fair play requires that she give up wanting her mother's man and wait for one of her own to come along. Her hopeful waiting for love ceases to be centered on her father and becomes focused on an outside love object, perhaps the boy next door. To repeat an important point, the girl's solution of the Oedipus complex is more complicated than a boy's for she begins with a homosexual relationship with her mother and ends with a heterosexual relationship with an outside love object.

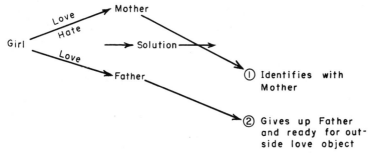

Fig. 2 Oedipus complex of the girl.

Abnormal solutions of the female Oedipus complex do occur. A girl may never give up loving her father and stay tied to him for life. Often such spinsters or maiden ladies have been courted by men and have had proposals but were unable to feel love for a suitor because they remained wholly attached to their fathers. No other man can ever mean anything to them. In less extreme cases, attachment to the father may be partially given up, and the girl can then love another man to a certain degree; she may even marry him. If so, she will never give herself to her husband completely, and he will soon tire of the relation, for every man wants his wife all to himself. Unhappiness, even divorce, is the usual result.

It also happens that a girl may never resolve her feelings of hatred towards her mother. As a woman, she may then have great difficulty in her relationships with other women who are in authority over her. As in the case of a boy, the whole process can be reversed which is called an inverted Oedipus complex—if the girl feels hopeful love towards her mother and an ambivalent love-hatred for her father. She will then identify with the latter and become masculine in her personality; she will desire a woman for a love object and become an active, overt homosexual, or *Lesbian*.

It is important to realize that if a parent dies or is absent, a substitute or surrogate is rapidly found. Uncle, grandfather, or big brother may substitute for father; aunt, grandmother, or big sister may substitute for mother. This substitution holds true for the solution of the Oedipus complex in both boys and girls.

The Oedipus complex is of extreme importance in determining the behavior, adjustment, and health of every individual. Much proof can be brought forth that the Oedipus complex and its normal and abnormal solutions exist as facts in the development of men and women. First of all, perhaps, is the proof afforded by psychologically sick persons who are miserably maladjusted and unhappy as the result of an improperly resolved Oedipus complex. Psychiatrists have found it possible to reason back from the wretched state of such persons to the original causes of their condition, and from there to what should have gone on during the formation and solution of the Oedipus complex. Thus, one might observe a hundred unmarried men in the admittedly abnormal state of bachelorhood and conclude that a man ought to give up his love for his mother and be able to form an attachment with a woman outside the family circle. A second proof of the reality of the Oedipal material can be found in the studies of children made by such groups as Dr. Gesell's at Yale. This group scientifically and objectively observed a number of children going through the developmental scheme. They documented the oral stage when only food mattered to the children; they noted the mothers teaching their infants bowel control and saw how important it was for the child to be loved and approved. During the genital stage they observed infantile masturbation and the unfolding of the Oedipal feelings. As the doctors observed the normal family life of the children, they saw a demonstration of how strongly the little boys wished their fathers would stay at work and how they longed to go to bed with their mothers; how the little girls' feelings towards their mothers became ambivalent and how they longed for their fathers to be their own husbands, their own men. What Dr. Gesell's group found has been confirmed again and again in further research. Many parents refuse to see what is actually taking place before their own eyes and may deny indignantly that their own children have experienced any of the emotions sparked by the Oedipal situation. Those who can be objective, though, will see in the development of every child the greatest proof of the Oedipus complex.

Psychoanalysis constitutes a third method for demonstrating the existence of the Oedipus complex. Psychoanalysis has two aspects, research and therapy, of which the first will be considered here. The psychiatrist's research into his patients' lives invariably uncovers definite proof of the existence of the Oedipus complex. Furthermore, doctors in training to become psychiatrists find that analysis of their own personalities is an excellent procedure. It is now routine for these perfectly well-adjusted and healthy men and women to have a thorough psychoanalysis. Information gained from the free association of ideas produced by these future psychiatrists has furnished another proof of the fact that healthy as well as sick people experience the Oedipus complex.

A fourth proof lies in material furnished in dreams, hypnosis, and narcosynthesis. As every student of psychology knows, a dream is a disguised expression of something taking place in the dreamer's inner self, in his unconscious mind. Dreams do not predict future events—to dream of a church does not mean marriage within a fortnight. Dreams are the result of unconscious effort to camouflage something the dreamer himself does not wish to face consciously. In dreams there occurs a significant symbolism in which the symbols are like actors acting out a drama on a stage. The symbols are usually sexual in meaning; for example, long objects represent the penis, as might be expected, while short, squat, hollow objects symbolize the female genital organ, the vagina. Using this range of symbolism, it is possible for a perfectly chaste young girl to express her sexual longings by dreaming of a windstorm on a hill which uproots a huge tree, carries it down the valley and throws it into her house. Having learned to interpret with considerable accuracy the significance of dreams, psychiatrists have found in their content further extensive proof of the existence of the Oedipus complex. Narcosynthesis, the inducement of a hypnotic trance by the use of Pentothal or Sodium Amytal, has also given dramatic evidence of the Oedipal situation. A patient under narcosynthesis or hypnosis will, at his doctor's instruction, revert to the age of four or five years and express verbally his feelings about his parents at that time. The material brought forth under hypnosis or narcosynthesis has invariably fallen into line with the Oedipus complex.

Only the known, tested and proved facts about the Oedipus complex have been presented here; the mass of unproved and doubtful theories concerning it has not been discussed. It has been seen that we possess unshakable evidence of its existence, and one final proof may be alleged. The known facts about the Oedipus complex do produce concrete results in working psychiatry. In its modern dynamic phase, psychiatry places the major accent on making sick persons well again. Frequently, this has been accomplished by understanding the Oedipus complex of the patient and by helping him to achieve a normal, healthy solution. The understanding of the Oedipus complex is one of the important tools of modern dynamic psychiatry.

RECOMMENDED READING

For complete bibliographic data, see also the General Bibliography following the Preface.

Abraham: *Selected Papers*, pp. 280-298, 338-369.

English and Pearson: *Common Neuroses of Children and Adults*, pp. 35-41.

Fenichel: *Psychoanalytic Theory of Neurosis*, chapter 6.

Freud: A Child is Being Beaten. *The Standard Edition*, Volume 17, pp. 175-204.

Freud: The Infantile Genital Organization of the Libido. *The Standard Edition*, Volume 19, pp. 141-148.

Freud: The Interpretation of Dreams. *The Standard Edition*, Volumes 4 and 5.

Hendrick: *Facts and Theories of Psychoanalysis*, chapters 2, 3.

Mullahy, P. *Oedipus Myth and Complex*. New York: Grove Press, 1955. (Paperback edition).

CHAPTER 4

Developmental Anatomy of the Personality

In describing the development of the normal personality, constitutional factors came first and then came two developmental factors: psychosexual or libidinal development and the Oedipus complex. A third developmental factor is known as the *developmental anatomy of the personality*.

This is a process which for all human beings begins at birth. In new-born children the anatomy of the personality consists of only one part, called the *id,* and for approximately the first year of their lives infants exist as ids, pure and simple. An id is a bundle of instincts which are by definition biological urges or biological needs. Thus, physiology and libido—previously defined as psychic energy—meet at this point in the child's life. Of the numerous biological urges, a few are the hunger instinct, the instinct for self-preservation, the sexual instinct, and the instinct to seek pleasant rather than unpleasant experiences. To elaborate on two of these urges: A new-born baby does not have to learn how to be hungry, for in him hunger is a biologically determined instinct. The urge towards self-protection is a part of every biological organism from the unicellular paramecium, which

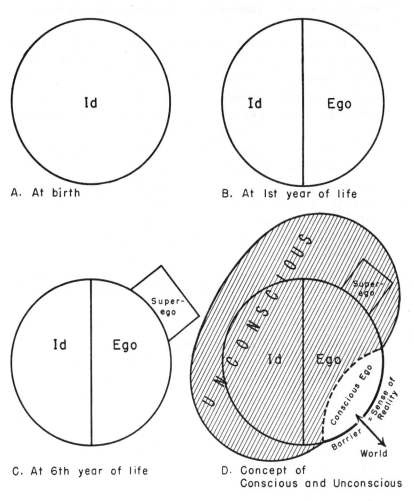

Fig. 3 Developmental anatomy of the personality.

scoots away from a jab by a needle, to the day-old baby who reacts by contraction when the table is struck on which he is lying—his instinctive attempt to protect himself from the blow. Scientific observation of infantile behavior has well substantiated the presence of the biological urges or id instincts.

The *ego*, or second part of the anatomy of personality, begins to develop towards the end of the first year of life. Ego, a term deriving from the Latin pronoun for "I," refers to the individual person, the self. Of the many theories explaining the development of the ego, the following seems to make the most sense. During the baby's first year of life his mother feeds him, changes his diapers, and gives the many other attentions necessary for his well-being. Her loving care for him, the intimate mother-child relationship, develops in the infant a feeling, a realization, that something is being done to him or for him by his mother. He becomes aware, for example, that his mother is putting the bottle in his mouth. Thus, little by little a cleavage or differentiation grows between them, so that eventually he realizes that his mother is the outside world and he the inside, that she is an object while he is the subject.

This differentiation, once begun, goes on to become ever more widespread. Prior to it the child had been one with mother, bottle, the entire world, willing and ready to suck on anything at all, mother's nipple, her breast, her thumb, his own thumb, his toe, a piece of feces, or a toy—it made no difference to him. No differentiation existed in his mind between himself and the external world as long as he felt that all was molded and fused into one unit. As his mother's loving care creates for him a sense of differentiation, the world takes form on the outside, and his self or ego on the inside. Thus, the greater an awareness people have of themselves, the greater is their awareness of the external world, and vice versa.

A third part of the anatomy of the personality, known as the *superego*, consists of the conscience or moral sense. The word *conscience*, meaning one's sense of right and wrong, should not be confused with *conscious,* soon to be introduced into the discussion. The superego develops from two sources. The earlier one lies in the anal stage of development when, in his bowel-training, the child first learns what he should and should not do, what is right and what is wrong. This gives rise to a "primitive superego" which sees things in terms of black and white, of right and wrong. The second source, coming in the genital period of life, is the child's identification with the parent of the same sex and is, therefore, part of the solution of the Oedipus complex. By identifying with father or mother, children develop an "ego ideal." Identification with a parent, however, accounts for only part of the development of the ego ideal. The moral and social code derived from contacts with the law, policemen, Sunday school teachers, public school teachers, the Girl Scouts and Boy Scouts—indeed, all of life—is added so that a social or mature superego is produced.

Another concept must now be introduced, namely, that of *the conscious* and *the unconscious.* By unconscious is meant anything concerning himself of which the individual is unaware. The superego is unconscious, the id is unconscious, and most of the ego is unconscious. The conscious part of the ego is the only part of the personality in contact with the outside world. An analogy might be a man steering a boat, aware only of the steering but not of the turbines going around or the propeller churning. An analogy of the relationship of the conscious and unconscious might be the one-tenth of an iceberg that is above water and in contact with the world, as against the nine-tenths that are beneath the surface.

It is possible to teach psychiatry, psychology, human behavior, or personality in terms of any of the three parts of the anatomy of the personality. When taught in terms of the superego, psychiatry sees the formation of personality in terms of identification with the parent; Adlerian[1] psychiatry can be said to be of this type. When taught in terms of the id, psychiatry explains personality by reference to the biological instincts; Meyerian[2] psychiatry can be said to be of the latter type. Most present-day psychology—the type found in this book—explains personality in terms of the ego; Freudian psychiatry is of this variety.

In order to understand an ego psychology, one must obviously examine the ego. Since the ego is a very important part of the personality, a great variety of ego functions must be described. First of these is preserving the sense of reality. The ego has to keep intact the barrier between the personality and the outside world, and cannot allow the barrier to diminish for a single moment; when the individual loses identity and fuses with the external world he becomes psychotic. Since the ego is the only part of the personality in contact with the outside world, its second function is perceptive. The ego feels all actions in the world. A kiss or a slap in the face, daylight, darkness, the weather—all occurrences outside the self—are perceived by the ego. Third, it

[1] Alfred Adler was born in 1870 and died in 1937. He became associated with Freud in 1902, but severed this relationship in 1911 to form his own group. From then on he championed the concept of *individual psychology*. He originated the term *inferiority complex,* referring to a basic psychological or organic inferiority. He tried to reduce all psychological phenomena to man's compulsion to strive for power. In his concept he included the influences of family and environment on the struggle for power over basic inferiority.

[2] Adolf Meyer was born in Zurich in 1866, came to this country in 1892, and introduced the best tradition of European psychiatry into the United States. He was professor of psychiatry at Johns Hopkins from 1910 until his retirement in 1941. He did not accept psychoanalysis but formulated the concept of *psychobiology.* This looks upon an individual in terms of his basic endowments, prefers to speak of reaction types rather than of individual diseases, and sees illness as an *experiment of nature.* He died on March 17, 1950.

has the executive function of determining what the individual says, how he acts, how he puts himself into the world.
A fourth function of the ego is to maintain *homeostasis*.
This fine descriptive term was coined by a physiologist named
Cannon who in studying physiology came to the conclusion
that all bodily functions seek to maintain a status quo, an
equilibrium. The term derives from the Greek adjective
homoios (meaning equal or the same) and the noun stasis
(meaning condition); thus, it applies to the process of main-
taining an even keel and minimizing stress. In a physiological
context, if an individual eats a bar of candy, the diffusion of
the sugar through the body represents the process of homeostasis. Examples are innumerable of how the body minimizes
stress and tries to keep the status quo. If a fat man walks
upstairs on a hot day, he will huff and puff to compensate
for the stress and strain but he will not drop dead from it.
The body's efforts to maintain homeostasis—the basis of the
metabolism of physical life—carries over into psychology.

We find one of the important functions of the ego to be
the maintenance of a comfortable state of equilibrium and,
thus, of happiness. How, it will be asked, does the ego maintain homeostasis, if an event occurs which causes the individual conflict, unhappiness or pain? The ego has many
mechanisms of defense, most normal of which is sublimation,
to be described first.

Sublimation simply means taking a middle course by giving in to both sides of the conflict; examples are easily found
in the daily activity of nearly every human being. A man may
have a hostile impulse to kill or hurt someone, anyone, but
will not go through with this because he would be punished
by society. His ego is beset by an id that says hurt or kill, and
a superego that says no. If he makes use of the defense
mechanism of sublimation by finding a middle course
through his conflict, he might become a surgeon, for in

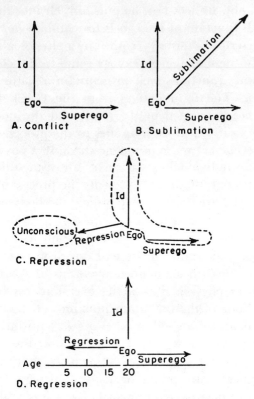

Fig. 4   Conflict and ego mechanisms of defense.

surgery it is possible to cut off arms and legs and make holes in someone's head, stomach, etc. The man would find in surgery great relief for his unacceptable impulse; and society, instead of locking him up, would not only approve but even pay him well for his effort. In this solution the two conflicting parts of his personality are involved equally: the hostility is satisfied; the superego appeased; his world is peaceful. The ego has done a good job of finding a *compromise*. Sublimation may also be used in solving homosexual conflicts. If a man has a desire to love another man rather than a woman, his superego at once says, "No—society will not permit such behavior." Let him once walk down the street swinging his hips or talking in a high voice, and people are going to call him a "fairy." Here again, the healthy ego may find a middle course between the desire and the prohibition. The man might become a barber or a masseur, because a barber can massage a man's face and a masseur can massage the whole body. In these occupations, instead of social disapproval and taunts, he would receive applause and remuneration. Of course, these examples do not imply that all surgeons are hostile, or that all barbers and masseurs have homosexual feelings.

If a girl is with a man who is very attractive to her, a sexual impulse may begin to come over her. She may begin to feel that she would like to have sexual intercourse, that marriage may be in the offing, feelings that are natural responses of her id to a very normal situation. Then, however, her superego may begin to demand restraint, telling her she cannot have intercourse because she must be a virgin when she gets married, raising the questions of what she would tell her mother, what she would do if she became pregnant, whether the man is clean, etc. An ego making use of sublimation would take a middle course between desire and prohibition, so that the girl might end up having a necking session, which would satisfy her sexual impulse and yet not go against the prohibition of her superego.

A student nurse on the ward who has just broken her sixth syringe for the day may well feel like chucking the nursing profession once and for all. Yet her superego will tell her that she is in an honorable profession with an excellent future, and that it is worthwhile to put up with some misery in order to reach that traditionally exalted status of a registered nurse. Following the middle course of sublimation, she would excuse herself quietly from the ward, go to the privacy of her room, take up a book and throw it with all her might and main at the wall. Or she might cuss and fume, but she would not hurl the syringe on the floor and give up nursing. This is what is meant by sublimation. A normal mechanism of defense, it is used every day in thousands of different ways.

Other defense mechanisms are not so normal. There is *repression* in which the ego literally shoves back or represses the conflict. A man may find in the course of a normal, happy life that his id will suddenly rear up and demand something. In the mechanism of repression his ego would reply, "I will pay no attention whatsoever to this demand. I will push it right back into the unconscious where it came from." The mechanism is illustrated by the boy who stuck his finger in a hole in the dike to hold back the sea; since he could not take it out for fear of the sea-water rushing through the opening, he was forced to keep an agonizing vigil. As this analogy suggests, repression gives rise to great tension, for without sublimation there is the constant strain of holding back the id impulse which is not being solved. The impulse is shoved back into his unconscious, but as soon as his ego relaxes, the impulse will come right back at him. He cannot afford to let go for a single moment, and the tension syndrome set up by such repression leads to constant fatigue and unhappiness. Repression, it could be said, "solves" the situation by not solving it.

An individual may bring into play still another well known mechanism of defense, called *regression*. He goes back to an early time in his life when his conflict did not exist. He may be twenty-two years old, for instance, engaged to be married but not quite sure of his feeling for his fiancée; or he may not wish to leave his mother; at any rate, a conflict of some kind arises. If his ego chooses regression, he will go back to the age of two or three when everything was pleasant for him, when he had no problems of earning a living, no demanding fiancée, no prospective in-laws, but did have a father and mother to take care of him. Regression of this type results in the mental illness of hebephrenic schizophrenia in which patients are childish and silly. Thus, in Shakespeare's *Hamlet,* Ophelia becomes insane in this fashion, playing with dolls and singing silly songs; but she ends up taking her life by drowning. Regression is not a normal mechanism of defense. Many other different mechanisms of defense exist. Psychiatrists can see the whole field of psychiatry in terms of the various ways in which their patients' egos handle the solution of conflict as compared to the ways selected by normal egos.

In the development of the normal personality a third and last factor exists that is composed of sociological or environmental elements—a hodgepodge of various influences upon the personality. Religious background, economic status, racial inheritance, etc., are grouped in this category. Jefferson said: "We hold these truths to be self-evident that all men are created equal; that they are endowed . . . with certain inalienable rights." Immediately after birth, however, a stratification of people begins which affects life, liberty, and the pursuit of happiness. Some people are "in," while others are "out." Being the child of John D. Rockefeller or of the village drunkard has a great effect on the individual personality. To be Catholic in a Catholic neighborhood or Jewish in a Catholic neighborhood—to fit in or to be excluded—is a factor in the growth of the personality; similarly, there is a difference in growing up as a Negro in a colored or in a white section. Education, jobs and professions, politics and clothing, all contribute to stratification. Karen Horney, among many other psychiatrists, is noted for her emphasis on the role of cultural, social, and environmental factors.

Constitutional factors make up the individual's inherited substratum of personality; developmental factors include his passing through the libidinal or psychosexual stages, his handling of the Oedipus complex, and the developmental anatomy of his personality; finally, the complicated sociological and environmental factors are superimposed. The result is the individual as he exists in the world at the present moment. Such is the process of development of the personality.

Before the various kinds of mental illness are described in the following chapters, it becomes advisable to mention a very interesting psychological ailment, known humorously to medical students as "second-year-itis," because it is endemic in the second year of their training. During the first year, study of the so-called basic sciences of anatomy, physiology, biochemistry, histology, etc., causes no emotional tension. But when students begin to learn internal medicine and pathology, many of them promptly develop "second-year-itis." When they read about a coronary heart failure, they feel in line for one; studying appendicitis produces the symptoms of that ailment; indeed, they may duplicate most anything in their textbooks. Similarly, the reader of this book should beware of identifying his emotions with any of the mental ailments as they are outlined. One of the best ways to avoid such identification is for the reader to check himself against normal personality—as highlighted in the following paragraphs—and then dismiss the question of his own normality from his mind while reading the rest of the book.

It is hard to define the criteria of normal personality

because the dividing line between normal and abnormal sometimes becomes very thin. Certain broad statements, however, can be made. As a first criterion of normality one might mention a sense of well-being; second might be the use of sublimation as the main mechanism of defense; third, the ability to postpone present pleasures for future ones; fourth, the presence of an intact sense of reality; fifth, good interpersonal relationships; and sixth, optimal adjustment. Although many more criteria could be listed, these six are in general the important ones.

A sense of well-being implies that the individual's tone is good, that he has, to use descriptive slang, "pep" and "oomph," that he is at least not completely "blah." He experiences an occasional ache or pain, an occasional fit of anger or gloom, but by and large he emanates well-being. Since the normal individual uses sublimation as the main mechanism of defense, the normal student nurse reading this book is not illegitimately pregnant, nor does she make a practice of having temper tantrums.

A normal individual can forego present for future pleasures, which is an important function of the mature ego. A student nurse willing to put off the present pleasures of dating or going to the movies two or three times a week in order to achieve the future satisfaction of becoming a registered nurse, presents a normal personality. A baby is unable to act in such fashion; he wants what he wants when he wants it and cannot wait an hour to get the same thing with less trouble.

To be concerned with what really exists in one's life is to have an intact sense of reality. For example, a student nurse is concerned not with a belief that the F.B.I. is after her, that she is a reincarnation of Cleopatra, nor some other unreal idea, but with her patients, studies, plans for Saturday night—the usual things in the life of a student nurse. Good interpersonal relationships make up the fifth criterion. Using the same example, the normal student nurse is not best friends with all of her roommates or classmates but she has, at least, one or two friends with whom she can converse. Since she relates on a friendly basis to a patient, a supervisor, or classmate, she is not empty, alone, or isolated—she has achieved good interpersonal relationships. The sixth and last criterion of normality consists of optimal adjustments to reality, the very best that can be made. If a person has no excessive social, religious, economic, or occupational problems, and no "drug hang-ups," he satisfies the demands of this criterion.

Any reader of the book may examine and evaluate his own personality in the light of these criteria of normality. Having come to the conclusion that he or she is a normal human being with a normal personality—remembering that there is frequently a thin line of division between normality and abnormality and that, therefore, considerable leeway exists in applying these criteria—the reader can safely proceed to the discussion of mental illness.

RECOMMENDED READING

For complete bibliographic data, see also the general bibliography following the preface.

English and Pearson: *Common Neuroses of Children and Adults,* chapter 1.

Fenichel: *Psychoanalytic Theory of Neurosis,* chapter 4.

Freud, A. *The Ego and the Mechanisms of Defense.* New York: International Universities Press, 1946.

Freud: The Ego and the Id. *The Standard Edition,* Volume 19, pp. 3-68.

Freud: Inhibitions, Symptoms and Anxiety. *The Standard Edition,* Volume 20, pp. 77-178.

Hartmann, H. *Ego Psychology and the Problem of Adaptation.* New York: International Universities Press, 1958.

Hendrick: *Facts and Theories of Psychoanalysis,* chapters 1 and 8.

Jahoda, M. *Current Concepts of Positive Mental Health.* New York: Basic Books, 1958.

PART   III

Illnesses of the Personality

CHAPTER 5

Schizophrenia: Definition and Description

First in importance of all the mental illnesses is schizophrenia, the most frequent cause of admission to mental hospitals. Known as a "protean" kind of disease, schizophrenia has many clinical pictures and clinical syndromes; it is a compilation, described by the terms *schizophrenia* and *dementia praecox*. The latter was invented in the 1860's by a French psychiatrist named Morel[1] who used it in the French version, démence précoce. It is descriptive in that the illness is truly a dementia (insanity) which occurs mainly in young people, as implied by the Latin adjective praecox (youthful). In 1911, a Swiss psychiatrist named Bleuler[2]

[1] Benedict Augustus Morel was born in 1809 and died in 1873. He pioneered in the social aspects of psychiatry, insisting on the frequent connection between undesirable environmental factors and mental disease. He was the first to use the term *dementia praecox*.

[2] Eugen Bleuler was born in 1857 and died in 1939. He is most famous for his work in the field of schizophrenia. Emil Kraepelin, a contemporary of his, had described the disease, classifying it into numerous types and subgroups, but Bleuler, profoundly impressed by the doctrines of Freud, transformed the disease from a descriptive clinical curiosity to an understandable, explicable, dynamic clinical entity, even substituting the term schizophrenia for dementia praecox. He was a prolific writer in the general field of clinical psychiatry and its philosophical background, but he is most recognized for his contributions to the understanding of schizophrenia.

devised the term schizophrenia from the Greek words schi-
zein (to split) and phrēn (mind or personality). It differs
from the earlier, purely descriptive name, "an insanity occurring in youth," in that it is a dynamic word which strives
to give some insight into the nature of the disease as a splitting of the mind or personality.

Since this book is dynamically oriented towards trying to
understand and thus help patients, schizophrenia will be
presented from Bleuler's point of view. He defined schizophrenia as a chronic, malignant mental disease process with
both primary and secondary symptoms, usually beginning in
the late teens and early twenties. Schizophrenia is *chronic*
in that it continues for a long time, like tuberculosis and
other long-standing physical ailments, as opposed to acute
illnesses. In labeling schizophrenia *malignant,* Bleuler meant
that it is incurable, that no one ever recovers from it, but the
important part of his definition is that he specifically labels
schizophrenia a malignant *mental disease process.* To understand this concept one must turn first to physical medicine.
In the case of rheumatic heart disease, for example, two
processes occur: first, the mitral valve of the heart becomes
pathologically involved in the rheumatic process; and secondly, there are in addition symptoms of dyspnea, orthopnea,
edema, etc. Although these symptoms are treatable, the pathology of the mitral valve itself is not. The same concept
applies to cirrhosis in which the liver becomes enlarged, the
cells multiply, and the liver hypertrophies, blocking the
portal circulation so that swelling of the abdomen results.
Treatment consists of eliminating the symptoms; one does
not touch the liver or reduce it to its original size. As is true
in these and many other physical diseases, the underlying
pathology, the basic disease process of schizophrenia is incurable and cannot be altered. It is chronic and malignant.

When Bleuler added to his definition that schizophrenia usually begins in the late teens and early twenties, he meant the age-group from sixteen to twenty-four. There are, however, many persons in whom schizophrenia begins in the late thirties and early forties. Whether or not the disease occurs in children is still debatable, although a great many psychiatrists believe that it does. At any rate, the great majority of cases do occur in the age group indicated by Bleuler. According to Bleuler the disease contains both primary and secondary symptoms, which needs further explanation. The *primary symptoms* are those of the underlying chronic, malignant process; in other words, they constitute the pathology of schizophrenia, just as involvement of the mitral valve or the enlarged liver constitutes the pathology of rheumatic heart disease or cirrhosis. The primary symptoms of schizophrenia as outlined by Bleuler are all splits, since it is by definition a splitting disease. First of all comes a *split of affect,* a word defined previously as equivalent to the patient's mood, feelings or emotions. For normal people thoughts and feelings run parallel. If they think of something sad, an appropriate feeling or affect of sadness accompanies the thought; similarly, an affect of happiness accompanies a pleasant thought. But in schizophrenia, affect splits away from thought, one going one way and one the other; thought and affect become *separated.* The schizophrenic patient may appear apathetic or cold because his affect, split off from the main stream of consciousness, is no longer available for use in relating to people. Since very little emotional rapport can be established, it is difficult to reach the schizophrenic in conversation. In addition, his thoughts are often accompanied by inappropriate affects. He may laugh and be happy when someone in his family dies. It is the schism between the emotional and the intellectual life of the patient that causes these odd emotional responses.

Next occurs a *split of associations*. Since in normal personalities there are links or associations which hold thoughts or thinking processes together, the normal thought pattern can be expressed as follows, the dashes representing links or associations between the thoughts:

Thought A——Thought B——Thought C.

For instance, a student in class might think, (A) "It's warm in the classroom today."——(B) "I wish the window were open."—— (C) "I wish this lecture were over." The links or associations between A, B, and C make the pattern of thought sensible and logical. A schizophrenic patient, however, might think, "Well, it's a warm day today." "I wonder what's for supper tonight." "I haven't paid my income tax yet." To this kind of thinking one cannot apply the clear, logical A——B——C sequence of normality. Since no logical links or associations exist between the separate thoughts, they are simply isolated units, a notation for which might be:

Thought A. Thought Y. Thought P.

This phenomenon, known as *disassociation,* is very characteristic of the schizophrenic patient who is likely to give almost any kind of answer. Asked about the weather, he may reply with an observation about today's ball game. This schizophrenic way of failing to hit the nail on the head varies from tangential associations to totally irrelevant responses.

Third is a *split of attention,* of the ability to keep the mind focused on any one subject. Normal individuals can sit at a lecture, watch television, listen to a concert, see a movie, or read a book, keeping their attention focused on the event. In the schizophrenic patient, however, capacity for attention splits so that his attention is directed to many different things at the same time, while he is unable to control and focus it on a single activity even if he wants to do so. The result is that the schizophrenic patient is preoccupied.

He can be seen in a hospital ward sitting in a corner reading a book, but he may not turn a page in an hour, or he may be holding the book upside down. His attention is somewhere else; he is thinking about something or feeling some emotion—possibly having an hallucination or delusion (page 70) —or looking out the window; these activities may be going on simultaneously. In diagnosing the disease it is important to realize that inability to concentrate is very frequently an early symptom of schizophrenia. Thus, a college student with incipient schizophrenia might remark: "I've been getting all A's so far, but, gee, for the past six months, I've been sitting in class and haven't been able to pay much attention. I just can't concentrate. It's as though my thoughts were going askew, as if they were no longer under my control. When I look at a page of a book, I can't focus my mind on it."

The fourth *split* in this disease involves the *sense of reality* and is perhaps the most important one to occur in the schizophrenic process. Normal individuals have egos, ids, superegos and the external world. For them the barrier between the ego and the external world is their sense of reality, for that is what marks them as intact personalities. In schizophrenia this barrier cracks or melts, and as the sense of reality disappears so does the sense of individuality. Melting into the outside world, the individual and the world fuse into a unit. From this phenomenon arise some of the most significant symptoms of schizophrenia.

First appear *ideas of reference*: the patient refers to himself things or events occurring in the outside world. For example, he might in walking along the street come to a corner where three men in front of a bar-room are arguing about a prize fight, Viet Nam or taxes. That these men are arguing about any such topic could never enter the mind of the schizophrenic patient, because he and the external world have become one. They must be talking about *him*.

That people are talking about him, or looking at him, etc., is a very frequent idea of reference in the schizophrenic, and arises from a split sense of reality. To give another example, someone might bang his fist on a table in a ward where a schizophrenic patient is sitting; the patient will react as if *he* had been slapped, since he and the external world are fused. A nice idea of reference occurs in the old joke about the lady at the racetrack who had just broken the elastic on her bloomers. Distraught, she ran from one person to another asking for a pin to hold them up. Suddenly the loudspeaker blared, "They're off," and she fainted.

As the sense of reality disappears in the schizophrenic patient, *panic* and *Weltuntergang dreams* appear. Normal people know who they are, where they are, what the world is, that it is light or dark, that they are in a room with green wallpaper, etc. They have some certainties, at least, to rely on, but in schizophrenia all such information is lost. The patient does not know exactly where he is, what the color of the walls of the room is, whether it is light or dark, what it feels like to be in love, to be kissed, to be slapped, etc. All the elements of reality tumble, disintegrate and disappear. Since the experience of losing the sense of reality is indeed terrifying, it is no surprise that many schizophrenics develop tremendous fear. Panic would be a more accurate description of their terror. They cannot describe what happens, but only state that what was here yesterday is not here today and that something is lacking or has changed. *Weltuntergang dreams,* which emerge as the sense of reality is lost by the schizophrenic patient, are dreams of catastrophe, of a "world going under," as the German term implies. One patient dreamt of an earthquake in New York City and of all the buildings crumbling and sinking into a bottomless pit. In just such fashion everything in the mind of the schizophrenic patient is disintegrating and slipping away, leaving him without a hold on reality. These dreams are completely characteristic of the disease at this stage.

As the real world slips away, a substitute world comes in to take its place, a world created by the patient and made up of things of special significance to him which are quite incomprehensible to the normal individual. So important are these inventions that the special name of *autisms* is given them. Although psychiatrists do not completely know the autistic substitute world, they do know some of its ingredients. It consists, in part, of peculiar, individually significant ways of thinking, acting, speaking, etc. So-called concretized thinking is apt to occur in which the thought processes are concrete rather than abstract. Various stereotypes of action are seen. The patient invents neologisms, words with wholly personal meaning and significance; he might devise a word like bushthrower and proceed to talk about bushthrowery by the hour.

Secondary symptoms of schizophrenia are defenses or attempts at halting the disintegrating process of the disease which entails loss of reality; these symptoms are attempts at restitution and, therefore, entirely different from primary symptoms. Drawing again the analogy with internal medicine, one sees that it is the secondary symptoms which are clinically visible. In a destructive heart ailment the edema shows the attempt of the body to get along with a damaged heart; by taking strain off the heart itself, the edema allows the patient to live. Such secondary symptoms, although signs of the ravages of a disease, are also evidence of the attempts of the body to get along under the handicap imposed by the underlying disease. The changes or symptoms one sees in cirrhosis and nephritis are likewise the body's attempt to correct or defend itself against the basic process of the ailment. So it is with schizophrenia.

Four types of secondary symptoms or defenses give psy-

chiatrists a basis for the diagnostic categories of schizophrenia. In the first or *catatonic* type of schizophrenia the mechanism of defense is denial. The patient, whose ego is melting
away, whose sense of reality is disappearing, who can no
longer think or concentrate, will deny this terrifying process
in one of two ways: either by becoming over-active and excited in an attempt to push the world away, or by withdraw-
ing from the world into himself. The one kind of denial,
known as catatonic excitement or furor, is indeed a true
furor; the patients are really maniacal. When lay persons
think of someone going crazy, running amok, they have this
kind of insanity in mind. Such a patient is so excited that
his whole being is active at one and the same time; simultaneously he kicks, screams, thrashes about, defecates, urin-
ates in a blind, raging attempt to kick the world away, to
blot it out, and to deny that anything is wrong. Patients of
this type may not stop the furor to eat and so starve themselves to death, or they may die from exhaustion, or from
knocking their brains out against a wall, although they are
not really suicidal. Seeing a schizophrenic patient in a catatonic furor is all that is needed to impress on anyone the
fact that this is a very serious disease, true insanity.

The other way of denying a loss of the outside world
is to withdraw to a state of absolute silence and isolation
in which the world is *shut out* rather than pushed out. In
this mute type of catatonic schizophrenia patients refuse to
open their mouths to be fed and do not respond at all to
questions. They sometimes exhibit the state of *cerea flexibilitas,* or waxy flexibility, in which their hands, feet, or
whole body can be put in postures which will be maintained
for a long time. Although the limbs of a patient in catatonic
withdrawal can be moved, they exhibit an indifference like
that of wax or tallow. If one lifts his hands above his head,
the patient will hold them up for hours on end, almost as

though hypnotized, as if in losing contact with reality he
had lost his sense of gravity as well. Such persons, like hypnotized persons, can do tremendous and superhuman things,
for they are not inhibited by the awareness of reality which
restricts the actions of normal persons. Since they often refuse to accept food, they may die from malnutrition. Such
patients may develop orthostatic edema from standing so
long in one position that all the fluids go to the legs which
may become secondarily infected. Thus, both types of catatonic schizophrenia are very serious and possibly fatal in
their effects.

The second type of secondary symptom and second variety of schizophrenia is called *paranoid*. Here, the mechanism
of defense is projection, or transferring to the outside world
something taking place within the patient. Projection is the
reverse of an idea of reference; in the latter something going
on in the external world is referred to the self, while in projection something within the self is referred to the outside
world. It will be remembered that one of the functions of
the ego is to keep the contents of the unconscious mind from
bothering the personality—in other words, to make the unconscious *stay* unconscious, to keep the repressed repressed.
Examples of such necessarily unconscious content are the
homosexual feelings and murderous impulses toward their
parents which all children experience at one time or another, and which are too disturbing to remain in the conscious mind. When an ego begins to disintegrate, as it does
in schizophrenia, when the personality loses its hold on the
external world of reality, the ability to keep internal feelings
and impulses unconscious or repressed is also lost. When
these contents of the unconscious mind start bubbling up
to the surface, they are too terrifying for the patient to
handle within himself. He begins to project them onto the
outside world; so he can be angry at a world which thinks

him to be a homosexual, a much easier escape than to face the fact that the homosexuality really exists within himself. Such thoughts and feelings from the patient's unconscious, projected onto someone else and then directed back to himself, make up the delusions and hallucinations characteristic of this type of schizophrenia. Paranoid, from the Greek words para (beside) and nous (mind) means literally "thinking beside the truth;" hence, it signifies error or delusion.

A great many examples of false beliefs or *delusions* are seen in schizophrenia. There are persecutory delusions in which the individual believes he is being pursued by the Masons, F.B.I., Communists, Democrats or what have you, though there is, of course, no foundation in reality for his conviction that someone or something is out to get him. In somatic delusions, which are false beliefs about the patient's body, he may believe his heart is falling out, his stomach has turned to cement, that there is poison in his blood, that spiders are crawling under his skin, and so on. Everyone has heard of the delusions of grandeur in which patients believe themselves to be very grand and very wonderful. Such patients often believe that they have a million dollars, own six Cadillacs and three newspapers, or that they are historic figures, such as Napoleon, Julius Caesar, or one of the Kennedys, or even God himself.

Hallucinations, on the other hand, are false sensory perceptions in which the patient perceives through one of his sensory organs something which does not exist in reality. Hallucinations affecting all the various senses have been observed. In auditory hallucinations the patient hears unreal sounds, perhaps a voice that is saying pleasant or unpleasant things to him, frequently with sexual or religious implications. There are visual hallucinations in which the patient sees unreal sights, such as a non-existent portrait of God or Christ hanging on the wall of his room, or even has the vision of a dead mother or father. Gustatory or taste hallucinations cause the patient to taste something which is not really in his mouth, while tactile hallucinations make him feel objects which do not exist. Delusions and hallucinations comprise the most characteristic symptoms of paranoid schizophrenia, especially persecutory delusions and auditory hallucinations.

In addition to the paranoid type of schizophrenia there is another disease, called *true paranoia* or *paranoia vera.* This is such a rare and debatable entity that it is not discussed here. In brief, it is a disease characterized by the presence of only one delusion or delusional system with the rest of the personality remaining intact—this, indeed, is difficult to picture.

In the third type, known as *hebephrenic schizophrenia,* the defense mechanism against the primary process consists of regression, or going back. If the primary process of losing his world occurs in a twenty-two year old patient, he can go back to a time when his world was secure. As pointed out above, Ophelia in Shakespeare's *Hamlet* did just that. Patients with hebephrenic schizophrenia are silly and childish; they laugh and giggle, although schizophrenia is a very serious disease with absolutely no humorous aspects. Such patients gesticulate wildly and make all kinds of facial gestures. Their hallucinations are perhaps the most vivid in all the realm of schizophrenia, so insistent and demanding that these patients often look up and talk to the wall because to them something is really there. Childishness, however, is the main characteristic of hebephrenic schizophrenia.

There is a fourth variety of schizophrenia, called the *simple type,* in which there is no defense mechanism. Since only the primary symptoms are seen in this type, the afflicted person has a dull and inappropriate affect, his associations are not up to par, he cannot focus his attention, and has no

ambition or goals in life. This form of schizophrenia often
produces a sort of hobo personality that floats through society from one place to another with no purpose in its existence. Such people cannot see making a living as a goal;
life has no real zest for them; they live—to use a wonderfully
descriptive phrase—in an ivory tower. The fact that people
confine their living to an ivory tower of one shape or another
is rather indicative of simple schizophrenia. Psychiatrists
often wonder whether the diagnosis might not apply to many
of the twelfth-year graduate students of ancient hieroglyphics,
secretaries whose lives are wholly absorbed in working for
their employers, or the accountant or research scientist
whose existence has become a mere matter of decimal points
and laboratory experiments. The current "drug scene" and
"hippie movement" probably contain many simple schizophrenics among their members.

It has been shown in this chapter that schizophrenia is
a disease having primary symptoms deriving from the basic
disease process, and secondary symptoms that are attempts at
defending against the primary process. The secondary symptoms predominate the clinical picture, but primary symptoms can usually also be seen. Since this is a disease process
in a state of flux, a patient may show predominant evidence
of projective delusional (paranoid) symptoms on one day, of
regressive (hebephrenic) symptoms on the next, and of
symptoms of denial and withdrawal (catatonic) on the third
day. Of the various kinds of schizophrenia, the paranoid type
is most common, second comes the catatonic variety, with
hebephrenic schizophrenia a close third. The simple type
is least often diagnosed and least often seen in hospitals:
individuals afflicted with it, being at worst bums or hoboes,
at best, solitary recluses, cause society little or no bother.
Paranoid schizophrenics, on the other hand, do give trouble,
for society is disturbed by an individual who keeps calling

the police with a long tale of persecution, or puts bars on the windows and refuses to leave the house. Society cannot tolerate catatonic or hebephrenic schizophrenic behavior patterns, which are very disturbing or even dangerous to the world at large. Sometimes the specific category is not clear and it may then be impossible to assign an exact diagnostic label. For the psychiatrist, however, this would be of secondary importance since his primary aim is to work with his patients, to try to understand them, and through understanding, help them.

RECOMMENDED READING

For complete bibliographic data, see also the General Bibliography following the Preface.

Batchelor: *Henderson and Gillespie's Textbook of Psychiatry,* chapters 11 and 12.
Ewalt and Farnsworth: *Textbook of Psychiatry,* chapter 20.
Fenichel: *The Psychoanalytic Theory of Neurosis,* chapter 18.
Freud, S.: Psychoanalytic Notes upon an Autobiographical Account of a Case of Paranoia. The Case of Schreber. *The Standard Edition,* Volume 12, pp. 3-84.
Hill, L. B. *Psychotherapeutic Intervention in Schizophrenia.* Chicago: University of Chicago Press, 1955.
Kolb: *Noyes' Modern Clinical Psychiatry,* chapters 25 and 26.

CHAPTER 6

Schizophrenia: Etiology and Treatment

A complete description of schizophrenia calls for much information in addition to that given in the previous chapter. It is well known that in the United States more hospital beds are devoted to psychiatric illnesses than to all other diseases combined. Of the beds devoted to mental patients, the majority is for those afflicted with schizophrenia, which thus constitutes a most important problem for American medicine.

Schizophrenia strikes males and females in an equal ratio. The curve in age distribution for this disease is bell-shaped, indicating that the majority of cases occur between the ages of sixteen and twenty-four, with others scattered on both sides of this period. Schizophrenia admits no distinctions of race, color, religion or nationality, striking equally throughout all groups.

Speaking of the etiology or cause of schizophrenia, psychiatrists are forced to state that they simply *do not know*. It takes courage to admit that the cause of such a frequent and important mental illness is unknown; indeed, honest admission of ignorance often arouses hostility in students taking up psychiatry for the first time. They demand to know how a psychiatrist can talk about a mental illness when he doesn't know exactly what it is or what causes it. Fresh from the study of medicine, a student sometimes comes to reason according to the formula, A plus B equals C; for example, that a pneumococcus plus a person equals pneumonia. The psychiatrist then might discuss this concept with the student and may ask him, for instance, to state what he knows about diabetes, specifically, its cause. "That's easy—lack of insulin," the student answers. "What causes deficiency of insulin?" asks the psychiatrist, and the student recites: "We can prove by autopsy that the Islets of Langerhans in the diabetic pancreas are atrophied and do not produce the required insulin in the body." When asked further, why the Islets are atrophied, the student, forced to admit ignorance, will see that he has been describing the pathology, not the etiology of diabetes, and that his knowledge does not suffice to explain why Mr. X should have diabetes but not Mr. Y. The psychiatrist may go on to repeat an anecdote of the early days of medicine. Koch and Pasteur were trying to prove the theory of germs, when a man came forward who was very skeptical and scornful of the new concept. "Diseases are caused by devils," he proclaimed, "not by what you call germs. Prepare a batch of the most virulent of these germs of yours, and I will drink it down right here in public." The scientists agreed on condition that he sign a statement taking full responsibility for his action. He agreed, drank the dose of germs and suffered no ill effects whatsoever—because he happened to be immune to the germs. In those days, scientists knew nothing about immunity.

Knowing the etiology of a disease includes a complete understanding of all *contributing factors*. These comprise all the elements involved in producing the disease in a specific patient. Pneumonia, for example, is no longer de-

scribed as the result of a person plus a pneumococcus. The
concept of factors makes it necessary to describe pneumonia
in terms not only of a person and a pneumococcus, but also
of his state of immunity, his resistance, the barometric pressure, the temperature, and innumerable other factors. When
those pertinent to any individual case are put together, the
etiology of the pneumonia is complete.

Applying this concept of etiology to schizophrenia, psychiatrists are able to say that they know some of its causal
factors. First come *organic or physical factors* such as various
kinds of brain disease, whether demonstrable clinically, mi-
croscopically or grossly, whether toxic, infectious, traumatic
or resulting from tumors. Some cases occur after taking
hallucinogenic drugs like marijuana, hashish, LSD, etc.
Constitutional factors of body build and version are included
in this group, for statistics show that many schizophrenics
are asthenic and and introverted. Then there are hereditary
considerations, endocrine changes, metabolic data, the general physiological functioning of the body, its specific reactions to stress situations, and many other elements.

Psychological factors constitute another large group. In
regard to them two explanatory theories are current. The
first theory has been formulated in terms of *lack of love in
childhood.* In describing the anatomy of the personality, it
was stated that the ego is formed as a result of the love received by the child from his parents; he develops a subject-
object differentiation as he comes to feel that he is an individual being loved by other individuals. If love is totally
or partly lacking, it is logical to assume that the individual's
subject-object differentiation will be less acute, that he will
have a weak rather than a strong ego, and that such an ego
is susceptible to breakdown and disintegration. The second
theory involves *stress and strain,* expressed in terms of
factors that impose themselves on an individual during his

life, the most noteworthy occurring at the time when he begins to show symptoms of schizophrenic illness. Psychiatrists find that what is a stress to one individual may not be a stress to another. Usually a stress is a disturbed equilibrium between the patient's needs from the important people in his life's orbit and their ability or willingness to satisfy these needs. Psychiatrists frequently combine the theory of lack of love in childhood with that of stress and strain, and some psychiatrists think that organic or physical factors are as much a cause of weakening the ego as are psychological stresses and strains.

Whatever specific view of the etiology of schizophrenia the psychiatrist endorses, he will usually admit that it is composed of two large groups of factors, the organic or physical and the psychological. Bellak well described another contribution to the etiology of the disease: if one examines carefully a thousand schizophrenic patients in regard to their anatomy and psychology, it is possible to plot on a graph the varying percentages of organic and psychological factors. The result is a bell-shaped curve in which one or two patients may possibly be 100 per cent psychological and 0 per cent organic, and one or two 100 per cent organic and 0 per cent psychological; about 80 per cent of the patients will be represented by various mixtures of organic and psychological factors. This corroborates the concept that schizophrenia is caused in most cases by a combination of factors.

Current concepts of the treatment of schizophrenia stress the planned use of the hospital environment, psychotherapy, and chemotherapy. The physical facilities of the hospital, the tangible and intangible atmosphere of the ward, the attitude of personnel toward the patients, the caliber of the nurses, attendants, occupational and physical therapists, dieticians, chaplains, and even the telephone operators, are all considered important aspects of the therapeutic milieu which can either abet or hinder the patient's recovery. It has been found that warm attitudes of acceptance of the patient and the understanding of untoward behavior, along with a prevailing spirit of optimism and enthusiasm, comprise the optimal therapeutic atmosphere for the schizophrenic patient.

Within this over-all therapeutic community, the hospitalized schizophrenic patient has the best chance of being helped by psychotherapy and chemotherapy. Psychotherapy for the hospitalized schizophrenic patient begins when he is offered a relationship or interpersonal experience with an individual who is permissive and non-critical, who passes no judgment and who accepts whatever the patient does, feels, thinks and says. Once the patient has accepted this relationship, a therapeutic situation has been established which can then be used for additional benefits and gains for the patient. Therapy, for example, can strengthen the patient's sense of reality (a process sometimes called *increasing reality· testing*) or can help the psychiatrist understand the patient's drives and conflicts with a view to helping the patient to understand himself (*insight therapy*). Often this psychotherapeutic process is attempted through group therapy instead of, or in addition to, individual psychotherapy.

The advent of chemotherapy, with special reference to the Phenothiazine Group of drugs, has had a drastic effect on the admission and discharge rates in mental hospitals. It is a well-publicized fact that the patient population in mental hospitals has been steadily decreasing since the discovery of the phenothiazines. Restraints are now seldom necessary, and it is no longer essential for ward doors to be locked. Thorazine® (chlorpromazine), Stelazine® (trifluoperazine) , Sparine® (promazine) , Mellaril® (thioridazine), Trilafon® (perphenazine), and Compazine® (prochlorperazine) are among those drugs most frequently used in the treatment of schizophrenia. As the number of his hallucinations and delusions lessen, and as his periods of excitement decrease, the patient becomes more amenable to psychotherapy and can receive the maximum benefit from the therapeutic community of the hospital. It thus becomes possible for the patient to be discharged in a shorter period of time.

These new medicines have also made it possible for the psychiatrist to treat more patients outside of the hospital. Thus, we are now witnessing the development of day care programs, evening hospitals, half-way houses, and community clinics designed to provide after-care for the discharged mental patient. In some localities, where such advances are well-established, it has become possible to think in terms of eventually eliminating the large mental hospitals of the "storage warehouse" type.

Electro-shock treatment (E.S.T.) or electro-convulsive treatment (E.C.T.) is still prescribed in some instances for the treatment of schizophrenia. Following a pre-medication of Atropine, the patient is placed on a bed and receives a general anesthetic plus one of the muscle relaxant drugs. When a satisfactory level of anesthesia and muscular relaxation has been achieved, a gag is placed between the teeth, and electrodes applied to the temporal areas via a saline conducting medium. A registered, regulated, and carefully controlled electric current is then passed through the brain. Without the muscle relaxant, the patient would respond with an epileptic-like fit of the grand mal variety, but with the muscle relaxant the convulsion is modified so that the risk of dislocations and fractures is minimized. The patient is then artificially oxygenated until the effects of the muscle relaxant drug wear off, at which time the respiratory muscles can again function normally. It is possible to treat elderly or infirm patients as well as the young and physically healthy patients, and it is not unusual for such electrical treatment to be administered to patients on an out-patient basis.

Until recently, Insulin Coma Treatment (I.C.T.) was considered by many psychiatrists to be the treatment of choice for schizophrenia. As Insulin Coma Treatment is now more or less obsolete, it will suffice to say that the treatment involved injecting a daily increasing dose of insulin until a state of coma was produced. The patient was then maintained in this state of coma for a prescribed time, usually about one hour, when he was revived by either intravenous or intragastric glucose. Treatments were continued on a daily basis for several months. It was a dangerous treatment unless it was possible to utilize a large, highly skilled, and specially-trained team consisting of both doctors and nurses. At one time, it was the best treatment psychiatry had to offer the schizophrenic patient. The new advances offer easier, safer, and much more practical treatment methods.

Pre-frontal lobotomy, now a rare operation, was also used many years ago in some cases of schizophrenia. It was found that the procedure produced a calming effect on the patient, but it has been almost completely abandoned because of the recent advances in new treatment techniques.

These new techniques of psychotherapy, chemotherapy and electro-shock treatment can be used on an out-patient basis to maintain the schizophrenic patient in the community and to prevent the necessity of hospitalization. All these therapies—psychotherapy, chemotherapy, electro-shock treatments, etc., aim at strengthening the ego (*increasing ego strength*) so that mechanisms of defense can be employed which are more mature, more healthy, and socially more acceptable than those of denial, regression, and projection. There is still hope that some day a medicine will be developed which will reverse or prevent the ego disintegration— the *malignancy of the ego*—of the primary schizophrenic process itself.

At one time, it was easy to discuss the treatment of schizophrenia since the psychiatrist's therapeutic armamentarium essentially consisted of insulin coma, electric shock, and prefrontal lobotomy. With the advent of psychotherapy, chemotherapy, and the hospital environment itself, the subject of the treatment of schizophrenia became a more complicated and difficult matter. Although there are some psychiatrists who exclusively champion one or more of these therapeutic procedures, most psychiatrists see the treatment of schizophrenic patients as involving the problem of finding the treatment method that is best for each individual patient.

Any consideration of the *prognosis* of schizophrenia is dependent upon the criteria defining recovery from schizophrenia. Unfortunately, psychiatry was years behind the times in establishing these criteria, as the following facts show. Before the second World War, only 10 per cent of the schizophrenics admitted to mental hospitals were discharged; nine of every ten schizophrenic patients spent a lifetime of virtual incarceration. The reason for this deplorable state of affairs lay simply in the stupidity of the psychiatric criterion for recovery from schizophrenia, namely, complete absence of symptoms: the patient's affect, associations and attention had to be perfect, his sense of reality intact, he could not have delusions or hallucinations. An equivalent in physical medicine would be to keep a cardiac patient hospitalized until the murmur had disappeared completely. The country's general hospitals would soon be filled with heart cases if such a policy were followed. The second World War gave psychiatry a tremendous impetus; psychiatrists soon began to realize the necessity for changing the criterion of recovery in schizophrenia to the much more realistic standard of the patient's ability to adjust to society. They decided to stop being concerned over the fact that schizophrenic patients hear voices or have bizarre beliefs, and to concentrate instead on the patient's ability to get along in the community.

Psychiatrists are under no delusion that these discharged patients are cured, any more than doctors in physical medicine believe that patients with heart disease, diabetes, cirrhosis, nephritis, or any such ailment are ever cured. They do know that such schizophrenics have fulfilled the modern criterion of recovery: they can function in society as nurses, doctors, mothers, fathers, typists, laborers, elevator operators, and so on. It has been found that, in general, the paranoid and catatonic types respond best to treatment, while hebephrenic and simple schizophrenics make the least progress.

There are no really valid statistics as to the rate of recurrence of the disease, because it is extremely difficult to classify minor lapses or relapses in the great number of patients who have had psychotic breakdowns and have then been released into the community. Whether such relapses are recurrences of schizophrenia is very hard to decide. Modern psychiatrists consider the rate of recurrence or readmission to the hospital of little importance in dealing with schizophrenia. They concentrate instead on avoiding hospitalization and on getting the patient back out into life in the shortest period possible. They are obviously not treating the underlying disease process; rather, they are dealing with the secondary symptoms. When doctors in medicine treat the secondary symptoms of cardiac or hepatic decompensation, disregarding the heart or liver itself, their goal is to help the patient reach a state of health compatible with his functioning in the community. Modern psychiatry has established the very same criterion for recovery from schizophrenia—successful functioning in the outside world.

RECOMMENDED READING

*For complete bibliographic data, see also the General Bibliography
following the Preface.*

Action for Mental Health. Final Report of the Joint Commission on
Mental Illness and Health. New York: Basic Books, 1961.

Bellak, L. *Schizophrenia.* New York: Grune & Stratton, 1966.

Caplan, G. *An Approach to Community Mental Health.* New York:
Grune & Stratton, 1961.

Ewalt and Farnsworth: *Textbook of Psychiatry,* chapter 24.

Fromm-Reichmann, F. *Principles of Intensive Psychotherapy.* Chicago:
University of Chicago Press, 1950. Also published in paperback:
Phoenix P 49, 1960.

Goodman, L. S., and Gilman, A. *Pharmacological Basis of Therapeutics,*
Third edition. New York: Macmillan, 1965, chapter 12.

Greenblatt, M., and Solomon, H. C. *Frontal Lobes and Schizophrenia.*
New York: Springer, 1953.

Greenblatt, M., York, R. H., and Brown, E. L. *From Custodial to
Therapeutic Patient Care in Mental Hospitals.* New York: Russell
Sage Foundation, 1955.

Hyde, R. W. *Experiencing the Patient's Day.* New York: G. P. Putnam's
Sons, 1955.

Jones, M. *Beyond the Therapeutic Community: Social Learning and
Social Psychiatry.* New Haven: Yale University Press, 1968.

Kalinowsky, L. B. and Hoch, P. H. *Somatic Treatments in Psychiatry,*
Second edition. New York: Grune & Stratton, 1961.

Kolb: *Noyes' Modern Clinical Psychiatry,* chapters 32, 33, and 34.

Modell, W. *Drugs of Choice,* 1968-1969. St. Louis: C. V. Mosby, 1968,
chapters 10, 14, and 15.

CHAPTER 7

Mental Retardation and Organic Brain Syndromes

The second edition of the *Diagnostic and Statistical Manual of Mental Disorders* of the American Psychiatric Association defines *metal retardation* as subnormal general intellectual functioning which impairs learning, social adjustment, and/or emotional maturation. The *Manual* lists over sixty different causes and types of mental retardation, grouped under the general categories of mental retardation associated with infection, intoxication, trauma, metabolic disorders, postnatal gross brain diseases, unknown prenatal influences, chromosomal abnormality, prematurity, major psychiatric disorder, environmental deprivation, as well as a category for unspecified causes of mental retardation.

Individuals with mental retardation have low I.Q. scores. If the I.Q. is under 20, the mental retardation is profound; severe mental retardation has an I.Q. range of 20 to 35; moderate mental retardation has an I.Q. range of 36 to 51; mild mental retardation from 52 to 67; borderline mental retardation from 68 to 83. It must be emphasized that the level of the I.Q. score is only one tool in making the diagnosis of mental retardation and in assessing its severity. The diagnosis is made on the basis of an evaluation of the patient's developmental history, his present functioning in academic, vocational, and social areas, and his motor skills and emotional maturity, all in addition to the I.Q. score. Degrees of mental retardation range from people who cannot learn to feed and clothe and care for themselves to people who may be able to get through the first few grades in school and be self-sufficient.

About three-quarters of the mentally retarded are found to be in the mild group. They frequently are not recognized early enough to receive the full benefit of the help they need. In only 2% of the mentally retarded is the defect so severe that even the most favorable life situation cannot balance it and chronic institutionalization is required. Most of the borderline cases of mental retardation can be rehabilitated and maintained in the community, but they have to be helped to use every bit of their limited intellectual endowment to meet the numerous demands of life.

In treating mental retardation, attention is directed at the family, which should support and not burden the child's emotional development, and at the school, which should adapt to the child's tempo and potential. Ideally, the mentally retarded child can be helped to grow up into an individual who can adjust and work in the community in a socially competent manner. Special mention should be made of cases of mental retardation associated with phenylketonuria (a protein metabolic disorder) because in these cases cerebral damage can be limited by the use of a diet from which phenylalanine has been eliminated, and the mental retardation prevented.

The *organic brain syndromes* characteristically result from diffuse impairment of brain tissue regardless of the cause, and they may be psychotic or nonpsychotic according to the severity of functional impairment of the individual. The psychotic organic brain syndromes are those that are severe enough to interfere seriously with the patient's ability to meet the ordinary demands of life. They frequently require hospitalization in their acute forms, and they make up a substantial proportion of hospitalized patients in their chronic forms. Many patients with nonpsychotic organic brain syndromes can be cared for at home, especially children, who may be mildly hyperactive, easily distractible, somewhat impulsive, and who suffer from short attention spans, and the elderly, who may be mild-mannered, forgetful, and somewhat disorganized and disoriented.

Diseases of the brain fall into two clinical types, *acute* and *chronic*. The clinical picture of *acute organic brain disease* is characterized by fear and disorientation. Depression or elation, delusions and hallucinations may or may not be present, but the patient is always fearful and disoriented. This clinical picture is present in all patients with acute organic brain syndromes regardless of the underlying cause.

The clinical picture of *chronic organic brain disease* is quite different; it is characterized by *release phenomena*. Speech and behavior patterns that ordinarily are socially inhibited are released from the inhibitory process. Families of such patients will often say that the patient has shown a complete change in personality. Along with the release of behavior, one also sees evidence of neurological release: release of lower levels of cerebral functioning from the control of the higher centers. Examples are dysarthria (imperfect articulation of speech), incontinence (release of bladder control from the influences of higher centers), the Babinski reflex, etc. In every case of chronic organic brain syndrome evidences of release can be seen regardless of the underlying cause.

Since this book is devoted to dynamic psychiatry, only a few of the organic brain syndromes will be considered. *Alcoholism* is a frequent cause of organic brain syndromes of both the acute and chronic variety. Delirium tremens presents the classical example of acute organic brain syndromes. In delirium tremens the toxic effects of alcohol in the patient's central nervous system cause tremor, disorientation, and fearfulness. Usually, these alcoholic patients experience characteristic hallucinations that involve a very realistic perception of a distorted reality and therein differ from those found in schizophrenia. These frightening hallucinations of delirium tremens tend to become more intense in the dark, and it is for this reason that a light in the room is comforting to the patient. A light in the room would have no effect on a schizophrenic patient who was hallucinating. Typically a schizophrenic hallucination would be to hear voices that are *conceived* as coming from within the patient himself, while the patient with delirium tremens may hallucinate cigarettes on the floor and try to pick them up as if they were really there, or may hallucinate pink elephants and snakes in the room and try to run away from them— hallucinations that are *perceived* by the patient as existing outside himself. The same syndrome of disorientation and fear can be caused by many other intoxications, e.g., bromide, barbiturates, lead, manganese, marijuana, LSD, methamphetamine ("speed"), etc. It is seen also after trauma (post-traumatic syndrome), in many febrile processes (delirium associated with pneumonia), in the post-epileptic confusional states, in many cases of central nervous system infections (encephalitis, meningitis), and even in some cases of brain tumor and of degenerative processes of the brain. Certain effects of vitamin deficiencies also can be included, a good example being the acute dementia in pellagra. Acute alcohol intoxication and pathological intoxication are other acute brain syndromes associated with alcoholism.

Alcoholism may also cause Korsakoff's psychosis, which is a chronic brain syndrome associated with long-standing use of alcohol. It is characterized by impairment of recent memory which is covered up by confabulations (fabrications created by the patient) and by peripheral neuropathy.

Alcoholic hallucinosis (accusatory auditory hallucinations with a relatively clear sensorium), paranoid states, and alcoholic deterioration are other chronic organic brain syndromes associated with alcoholism.

The organic brain syndromes associated with *old age* may be either psychotic or nonpsychotic, as well as either acute or chronic. The presenile dementias in this respect are similar to the senile dementias, and it is frequently difficult to differentiate these two illnesses from the clinical picture seen with cerebral arteriosclerosis ("hardening of the arteries of the brain").

The effects of infection also can be psychotic or nonpsychotic as well as either acute or chronic. Encephalitis is usually associated with an acute delirium that may be characterized by emotional indifference, whereas meningitis and brain abscess may present the clinical picture of acute organic brain disease and then progress into the clinical picture of chronic organic brain disease. Infections with syphilis may be acute in the stage of meningovascular inflammation, but the clinical picture of general paresis (parenchymatous syphilis of the nervous system) is characteristic of the chronic organic brain syndromes. In general paresis, one sees the characteristic release of behavior from the controls of higher cerebral centers. For example, a bank president, the pillar of society and model of propriety, may become loose in his sexual behavior, may swear freely, etc. Delusions of grandeur are another well-known characteristic in general paresis.

To these should be added the organic brain syndromes associated with epilepsy, neoplasm, trauma, systemic infections, endocrine disorders, vitamin deficiencies, intoxications with drugs and poisons, etc. The hallucinogens and psychedelic drugs, such as marijuana and LSD, for example, alter the state of consciousness, interfere with the contact with reality, decrease the control over behavior, and impair the use of good judgment. In addition, the opiates may lead to loss of ambition and initiative as well as to problems of addiction. The organic brain syndromes represent an important and varied group of psychiatric illnesses. In acute and in chronic brain syndromes, treatment is directed at the underlying condition. However, psychoactive drugs are proving very useful in controlling the behavioral manifestations of such illnesses: for example, Librium® (chlordiazepoxide) and Sparine® (promazine) are used in treating acute alcoholism, and Thorazine® (chlorpromazine) and other phenothiazines are very helpful in senile psychoses. Chemotherapy can shorten the period of hospitalization and allow many patients to be maintained at home in their communities.

The legal and social implications of mental retardation and organic brain syndromes are tremendous. Although society has a responsibility to care for its mentally retarded members, special problems are created by the mentally retarded who commit crimes—the so-called "defective delinquents." It is hoped that new laws and legislative enactments will help solve some of the problems of the defective delinquents. The custodial care of the elderly members of society, especially those afflicted with chronic organic brain syndromes, is another special problem. Geriatrics—that subdivision of medicine and of psychiatry which is concerned with old age and its diseases—is a rapidly growing area of interest to many. Certainly, the care of the mentally retarded, of the elderly, and of those afflicted with chronic organic brain syndromes represents one of the greatest challenges facing psychiatry today.

RECOMMENDED READING

For complete bibliographic data, see also the General Bibliography following the Preface.

Alexander, F., and Ross, H. *Dynamic Psychiatry.* Chicago: University of Chicago Press, 1952, pp. 211-255.

Arieti, S. *American Handbook of Psychiatry.* New York: Basic Books, 1959, chapters 50-63.

Batchelor: *Henderson and Gillespie's Textbook of Psychiatry,* chapters 15, 16, and 17.

Ewalt and Farnsworth: *Textbook of Psychiatry,* chapters 7, 15, 16, and 17.

Kolb: *Noyes' Modern Clinical Psychiatry,* chapters 9-21.

Mezer, R. R., and Blotner, H. "Alcoholism." In *Traumatic Medicine and Surgery for the Attorney,* Volume 7, pp. 505-527. Washington, D.C.: Butterworth, Inc. 1962.

Mezer, R. R., and Rheingold, P. D. "Mental Capacity and Incompetency: A Psycho-Legal Problem." *American Journal of Psychiatry,* March, 1962, *118*:827-831.

Stevenson, G. S. *Mental Health Planning for Social Action.* New York: The Blakiston Division, McGraw-Hill Book Co., 1956.

CHAPTER 8

Psychotic Affective Disorders

In the category of affective disorders belong those mental illnesses in which affect or mood is primarily involved. First to be discussed is *manic-depressive psychosis,* which is by definition a benign, functional, affective illness marked by an innate tendency to recur, and which has two phases. It is not a malignant process like schizophrenia, but rather a self-limiting process; it is a *benign* disease from which patients do recover. Like schizophrenia, manic-depressive psychosis is not linked to any known organic cause and is hence termed *functional.* To describe it as an *affective* illness simply means that it primarily involves the mood, feelings, or emotions of the patient.

Thus, if the normal mood is thought of as a horizontal line, any involvement of the mood will show up either as a positive increase above or as a negative decrease below this level. In psychiatry the positive or increased phase is called *manic,* and the depressed or negative phase *depressive.* There is a constant variation in the mood of normal persons, all of

91

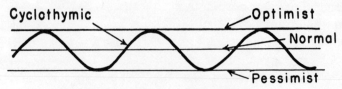

Fig. 5   Normal variations of mood.

whom experience days when they are a little happier than usual and blue Mondays when they feel down in the dumps, or, at least, not quite so happy as usual. Some people, always riding the crest of the wave, are habitually rather optimistic

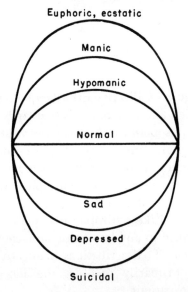

Fig. 6   Degrees of mood involvement in manic-depressive psychosis.

and happy, while others are "sad characters," habitually on the pessimistic side but not enough below the base-line of normality to be called mentally ill. A third group of people, known in psychiatric parlance as *cyclothymic,* alternate between these degrees of optimism and pessimism. A certain variation of mood is the normal condition of most people; a mental illness, however, arises when mood is involved to an abnormal degree. On the positive side there are abnormal degrees of involvement known as hypomanic, manic, and euphoric; the degrees of negative involvement are called sad, depressed, retarded, and suicidal. As a result of these characteristics, manic-depressive psychosis is sometimes called a plus-or-minus disease.

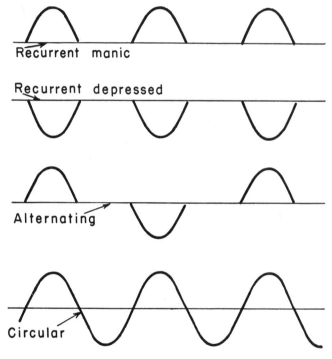

Fig. 7 Types of recurrences in manic-depressive psychosis.

The recurrences of manic-depressive psychosis occur in several forms or patterns. In the type known as *recurrent manic*, the patient has a manic attack, returns to the base line of normality, remains normal for a time, then experiences another manic attack, and so on. The victim of what is called *recurrent depressed* psychosis goes into a depression, returns to normality for a few years, experiences another depression, becomes normal for another period, and continues this pattern. In the *alternating* type of recurrence the patient has a manic episode, returns to the base line of normality for a few years, experiences a depression, returns to normality, and then repeats this process. The three types just described are characterized by the fact that periods of normality exist between the recurrences of illness. There is another type of recurrence, known as *circular,* which does not have intervals of normality. The patient has a manic attack, comes back to the base line of normality, but then goes directly into a depression, back to the base line, and again directly into a manic attack, repeating the pattern. By far the most frequent type of recurrence is the recurrent depressed psychosis.

Table 2   MANIC-DEPRESSIVE PSYCHOSIS

	Manic +	Depressed −
Mood or Affect	Happy, euphoric, ecstatic with hostility underneath	Sad, depressed, suicidal
Behavior or Activity	Laughing overactive ⟷ furor	Crying underactive ⟷ stupor
Thinking and Speech	Rapid thinking overtalkative ⟷ push of speech	Slow thinking undertalkative ⟷ mute

(Retardation)

Each phase of this mental illness involves (1) mood, (2) behavior and activity, and (3) thought and speech. In the manic phase they are all increased, but beneath the manic patient's happy exterior are to be found tremendous anger and hostility. He is overactive—in extreme cases literally producing a fury of activity, jumping all over the place, to use a popular phrase. So marked is the patient's excitement that it is frequently difficult for psychiatrists to distinguish the manic phase of manic-depressive psychosis from the catatonic excitement of schizophrenia: both kinds of patient may be seen flailing their arms, beating with their fists, kicking, spitting, urinating, defecating, laughing and crying, all at once. The usual manic patient, however, is not in a state of furor, but merely paces around the floor, cannot sit still and laughs a great deal. The speed of thinking and speech also increases in the manic phase. Keeping in mind the definition of normal thinking as a logical progression of thoughts connected by appropriate associations:

Thought A——Thought B——Thought C,

one can picture manic thinking as the same process except that the links between separate ideas are much shorter:

Thought A–Thought B–Thought C.

The total effect then becomes one of very rapid thinking. Unlike the schizophrenic's disassociated and disconnected thought process, that of the manic is perfectly logical and connected. Manic patients are quite literally individuals who "talk a mile a minute." This phenomenon is often known as *push of speech,* a very apt term as their speech seems to come out under pressure, one word pushing the other along. In the manic attack, then, the patient feels happy, is overactive in behavior, and exhibits rapid thinking and speech —all in varying degrees.

In the depressed phase of manic-depressive psychosis, on the other hand, behavior and activity decrease so that the patient is underactive and exhibits a facial expression of sadness, cries, or sits dejected in a slumped posture. Occasionally, he becomes underactive to the point of a stupor which is similar to and hard to differentiate from catatonic withdrawal in schizophrenia. Thinking is decelerated, the links or associations between thoughts becoming longer, so that the process consists of thought A followed by a long link to thought B, which in turn is followed by a long link to thought C, and so forth:

Thought A———Thought B———Thought C.

Speech in this condition often becomes slow and sparse; when asked how he feels, there is a very long interval before the depressed patient replies that he feels "lousy." This combination of underactivity with slow thinking and slow speech is called *retardation*.

As in the case of schizophrenia, psychiatrists have to admit that they do not understand the etiology or causality of manic-depressive psychosis; there are even fewer explanatory theories to fall back on than in the case of schizophrenia. Loss of love in childhood does not seem to be a factor; occasionally, but not usually, a stressful situation in the patient's life does play a part. Some interesting and challenging theories have been advanced, however. For instance, that depression can be defined as self-hate or introjected hostility—the hostility being introjected because of guilt; and that when the guilt is satiated by this self-punishment, the hostility is directed outward towards the external world and results in the manic attack. No known or detectable organic factors are present in manic-depressive psychosis. The few available clues, obtained mainly from the occurrence of the illness, do not give very satisfactory grounds for speculation: It is known that the illness is almost twice as common in women as in men, the ratio being five to three; further, that an hereditary factor seems to be involved, which was not true in schizophrenia where a schizophrenic family is a definite exception to the rule. In manic-depressive psychosis the illness often seems to be transmitted from one generation to the next, usually involving the female members of the family. The pre-psychotic personality frequently reveals a pyknic extrovert.

There was a time when most psychiatrists agreed that the treatment of choice for patients with manic-depressive psychosis was electro-shock treatment. Positive response in the case of depression was practically specific, and about 90 per cent of depressed patients responded favorably to electroshock treatment. The manic cases responded less well, with from 70 to 75 per cent showing improvement. Electro-shock treatment did not stop the recurrences of the disease, but did shorten the duration of each manic or depressive attack.

Recently, however, the use of anti-depressant drugs in the treatment of the depressed phase of manic-depressive psychosis has made the exact role of electro-shock treatment unclear. The psychoactive drugs used in the treatment of depression include the tricyclic compounds, such as Tofranil® (imipramine), Elavil® (amitriptyline), Norpramin® or Pertofrane® (desipramine), and Aventyl® (nortriptyline), and the monoamine oxidase inhibitors, such as Marplan® (isocarboxazid), Nardil® (phenelzine), Niamid® (nialamide), and Parnate® (tranylcypromine). The tricyclic compounds are more rapidly eliminated from the body thus allowing for a quick substitution to a monoamine oxidase inhibitor. The monoamine oxidase inhibitors, on the other hand, are slowly eliminated from the body and it is dangerous —indeed, it may even be fatal—to mix a tricyclic compound with a monoamine oxidase inhibitor. Furthermore, tricyclic compounds in general seem safer than the monoamine oxidase inhibitors. For these reasons, most psychiatrists prefer to try the tricyclic compound first, reserving the monoamine oxidase inhibitors for those cases which do not respond to the tricyclic compounds, and reserving electro-shock treatment for those cases which have failed to respond to either drug. Naturally, special circumstances or the patient's condition—for example, suicidal patients—may require early hospital admission and electro-shock treatment.

In addition, the use of the major tranquilizers of the phenothiazine type has proven effective in treating many cases in the manic phase of a manic-depressive psychosis. In some cases, as a matter of fact, the excitement, overactivity, and overtalkativeness can be controlled more quickly by parenteral phenothiazines than by electro-shock treatment. Indeed, it may even be possible at times to avoid hospitalization of the manic patient by use of psychoactive drugs.

Lithium carbonate is a recent addition to the therapeutic armamentarium available to deal with manic-depressive psychosis. It seems to work better in manic patients than in depressed patients, and it seems to be effective in preventing recurrences of manic-depressive illness. However, lithium carbonate is still in the experimental stage of development and is still being studied and evaluated. It has not yet been released for general usage in the treatment and prevention of manic-depressive psychosis.

As a result of electro-shock treatment and drug therapy, many manic-depressive patients become accessible for psychotherapy. In these cases, psychotherapy can help shorten the present attack or may be able to prevent recurrences. However, the exact value of any type of treatment of manic-depressive psychosis is difficult to evaluate on a realistic basis because these patients do get better on their own.

Prognosis is good, in the sense that the prognosis of each separate recurring attack is good. The chance of such recurrence is great but it cannot be predicted. For example, a woman of thirty-five, experiencing her first attack of depression, may consult a psychiatrist after the depression has been going on for six months. If she is treated at this point, she may recover completely in a matter of weeks, and then go for a day, a month, a year, or for the rest of her life without another attack of depression, although technically she should have one unless she happens to die first. Theoretically speaking, since this is a recurrent disease, every patient going through a first attack should have others; but psychiatrists cannot foretell how soon, nor even whether a recurrence will ever take place.

It is essential to take a practical view of the problem of suicide in manic-depressive psychosis. Although nobody, obviously, ever gets a chance to question patients whose suicidal efforts succeed, psychiatrists can talk to those who have tried and failed. From such observation it is clear that to commit suicide requires great courage, and that it is really a kind of extreme action. It is the ultimate in self-hate, but at the same time it is hostile toward the patient's family. Suicide does not occur when the individual is just becoming depressed, or when he is coming out of his depression, or at the depth of depression. Although the depth of depression 'would logically seem to represent the greatest danger, the patient simply does not have enough drive or energy to kill himself. The real danger point comes when he is sufficiently depressed to want to do it, bu not depressed enough to be so underactive and lacking in energy that he cannot. It is important, therefore, when treating a manic-depressive patient who is in the depth of a depression, to remember that the greatest danger of suicide will come as he begins to feel better. He must then be closely watched, because he will still want to kill himself, and as he begins to improve will gain sufficient energy to carry out the intention. There are important legal, social, and religious implications to suicide.

It used to be said that one need not worry about the suicidal person who talked of suicide. But, this idea has been proven to be incorrect. It has been shown that most suicidal patients do talk about suicide and do give adequate warning of their intentions. Thus, careful attention should be given to the person who talks of suicide. Many communities have programs to prevent suicide.

It should be added that many patients exhibit schizophrenic features along with the picture of a manic-depressive psychosis, while many schizophrenic patients have manic-depressive features—such patients are usually said to have a *schizo-affective psychosis*. The presence of affective components improves the prognosis of the schizophrenic, while the presence of schizophrenic components worsens the prognosis of the manic-depressive patient.

A second affective disorder, known as *involutional psychosis*, consists of two kinds, involutional melancholia and involutional psychosis, paranoid type. Both occur in the so-called involutional period which covers roughly the years from forty to fifty-five. At one time it was thought that the involutional period involves only women, that it is the time when the ovaries stop working, menstruation ceases, and women enter the menopause or physiological change of life; in the present discussion, however, this is not the meaning of involutional period. Rather, it refers to a stage in life, a psychological orientation or attitude common to both sexes, and characterized by introspection and mature reflection over the fact that youth is past, middle age is present, and death ahead. Psychiatrists now know that involutional psychosis sometimes occurs in women still having menstrual periods, and that it also occurs in men.

Involutional melancholia is a depression occurring in the involutional period—a mid-life depression—affecting females and males in equal numbers; it is free of retardation but characterized by the presence of agitation, and is thus also referred to as agitated depression. Like manic-depressive patients in a depressed phase, those with involutional melancholia exhibit varying degrees of sadness, but unlike the former, they are agitated, as shown in their tenseness, anxiety, restlessness and tremulousness. They will pace the floor, pull their hair, and wring their hands. They frequently suffer from insomnia and loss of appetite. Although the combination of depression and agitation does not seem logical, it is the prime characteristic of this illness. Such patients may also have delusions, frequently in the nature of false beliefs about their bodies: that their blood is turning to water, or that their stomach has turned to cement. Headaches, particularly the bandlike, constricting variety, are a frequent complaint among such patients. They often display nihilistic thinking in which pessimistic thoughts are combined with guilt feelings of sinfulness and wrong-doing. All of these symptoms add to their tenseness, agitation, depression, misery, and suffering.

Involutional psychosis, paranoid type, on the other hand, is a paranoid illness with or without depression and agitation, occurring in the involutional period, and affecting females and males in equal numbers. It is described as a paranoid illness because delusions, usually of a persecutory nature, and hallucinations are seen, just as in the paranoid variety of schizophrenia that occurs two decades earlier in life. The patients are usually, but not always depressed, and not so much so as the victims of involutional melancholia. Diagnosis in any given patient depends on whether the paranoid or the depressed component is greater.

The etiology of both involutional melancholia and involutional psychosis, paranoid type, is unknown. A few cases exhibit endocrine factors, and no one has found organic brain disease to be a frequent cause. The personality structure of the earlier life of patients afflicted with involutional melancholia ordinarily shows that they were very conscientious, overly clean and tidy, excessively punctual and stubborn individuals. A woman with involutional melancholia is often an excellent housekeeper. Patients with involutional psychosis, paranoid type, usually show shy, introverted, se-

clusive pre-psychotic personalities. In both types of involutional psychosis, emotional stresses and strains in the lives
of the patients constitute another psychological factor which
certainly cannot be overlooked; psychiatrists, however, are
again forced to admit that they are largely ignorant of the
causes of these diseases.

The treatment of involutional melancholia and of involutional psychosis, paranoid type, involves the judicious
use of tranquilizers, anti-depressant drugs or electro-shock
treatment in combination with psychotherapy. Patients with
involutional melancholia, though depressed, are agitated as
well, and therefore have enough energy to commit suicide.
Prompt psychiatric intervention can literally be life-saving.

The prognosis of patients with involutional psychosis,
paranoid type, is generally good; the prognosis for patients
with involutional melancholia is generally excellent. Although the latter diseases may recur, usually it is a single
episode in the life of a patient who can be promptly returned
to a happy and effective existence.

RECOMMENDED READING

*For complete bibliographic data, see also the General Bibliography
following the Preface.*

Batchelor: *Henderson and Gillespie's Textbook of Psychiatry,* chapter
10.
Bellak, L. *Manic-Depressive Psychosis.* New York: Grune & Stratton,
1952.
Ewalt and Farnsworth: *Textbook of Psychiatry,* chapters 18 and 19.
Hoch, P. H. and Zubin, J. *Depression.* New York: Grune & Stratton,
1954, chapters 1-6 and 12-14.
Kolb: *Noyes' Modern Clinical Psychiatry,* chapters 23 and 24.

CHAPTER 9

Neurotic Affective Disorders

The preceding chapters dealt with psychoses: the functional psychoses of schizophrenia, manic-depressive psychosis, and the involutional psychoses, as contrasted with the organic psychoses which result from organic brain disease or injury. An inclusive definition of psychosis will help the reader to compare it with and differentiate it from neurosis. The concept is one of the most difficult to put into words, because psychiatrists do not yet fully understand either psychosis or neurosis, and, because many borderline cases have both psychotic and neurotic features.

A working definition is that psychosis is a major mental illness often requiring hospitalization, involving the total personality of the patient, and having as its main characteristic the loss of contact with reality. This definition needs elaboration before it will give a reasonably full picture of psychosis. A mental illness that is serious and ominous is a *major* illness in the same sense that cancer is a major disease as compared with a boil, or pneumonia as compared with the common cold. Psychosis frequently requires hospitalization: society will not tolerate a paranoid patient who

locks the door and telephones for protection; society will
not condone those who try to kill themselves or who attempt
murder; equally unacceptable is the hallucinated patient,
or the patient who is in a catatonic or manic furor, or is
mute, withdrawn and immobile. In short, psychosis and
society do not mix. When psychiatrists say that psychosis
involves the total personality, they mean that most, if not
all, of the reactions comprising a patient's personality have
gone awry; the main characteristic of a psychosis, however,
is loss of contact with reality.

Insanity is a term which no longer has much medical
meaning. Modern psychiatrists refer to mental illness in
terms of neurosis and psychosis, and the "insane asylums"
are now called mental hospitals. The concept of insanity
remains meaningful to law: an insane person can be committed to a mental hospital, can be deprived of his civil
rights, can be declared incompetent to conduct his own
affairs or to make a will, and can even be excused from
punishment for criminal behavior. People can be psychotic
without being legally insane and vice versa.

Set against the definition of psychosis just given, neurosis
is an illness seldom requiring hospitalization, involving
a fragment of the total personality and characterized
by maintenance of contact with reality. Clearly, personality disorders involving only a fragment of the total
personality have very different meanings and consequences
from illnesses that involve the whole personality. Neurotic
patients are almost always treated in out-patient departments
or by private psychiatrists on an ambulatory basis. Society,
though somewhat troubled and bothered by neurotic complaints and actions, can usually tolerate them. No one gets
very upset about a neurotic because his contact with the
world is intact; while he may distort reality considerably, he
never wholly loses sight of it as does the psychotic.

There are additional minor differences between the two ailments. The psychotic patient is brought to the psychiatrist for help, while the neurotic comes of his own accord; there can be little empathy with (feeling into) the psychotic, but a great deal with the neurotic patient; psychiatrists do not know the etiology of psychoses and can only wonder why the patient is so depressed or why he hears voices, whereas they understand the cause of neuroses so thoroughly that often, when treating a neurotic patient, psychiatrists are made to feel: "There, but for the grace of God, go I!"

Psychiatrists are still disputing which, exactly, are the distinguishing characteristics of neurosis. Regardless of such clashes of opinion, the information of the preceding paragraphs is needed as background in discussing the illnesses in the affective group which are neurotic. First is *reactive depression,* a depression without retardation or agitation, developing in response to a situation in the patient's life. Although he is depressed, feels sad and weeps, he exhibits neither the retardation seen in the depressed phase of a manic-depressive psychosis, nor the agitation characteristic of involutional melancholia: his depression is simple and uncomplicated. Situations which precipitate this type of illness are varied—failing an examination, being "stood up" on a date, receiving bad news about the family, going bankrupt, losing one's home in a fire—in short, losses and catastrophes. The second edition of the *Diagnostic and Statistical Manual of Mental Disorders* calls such cases "depressive neurosis."

It must be noted that what overwhelms one person may not affect another person at all. It is wise, furthermore, to distinguish carefully between the normal and the neurotic reactive depression. The difficulties of normal living are bound to bring everyone face to face with disturbing situations. The normal response to these is a self-limited reactive depression of one or two days' duration which does not seriously affect the individual's adjustment and ability to work, but may interfere with such capacities as speed or concentration in working. A neurotic reactive depression, on the other hand, is a long-lasting one from which the patient cannot recover unaided, cannot pull himself up by his own boot-straps, as it were. Frequently, his adjustment is so disturbed that he cannot work.

Psychiatrists are delighted to say that—in this case—they do know the etiology of a reactive depression. There are two specific causes: the situation and the individual. When the causes are known, treatment of an ailment is naturally quite specific. Thus, in the case of reactive depression, treatment is focused on improving either one of the factors, and preferably both. Examples of improving the situation are: finding financial aid for a man who goes into a reactive depression because he is out of work and cannot support his wife and children; or, if a girl develops a reactive depression when the man she loves deserts her, directing her thoughts toward finding another suitor. In the course of treating such problems, psychiatrists frequently find occasion to seek practical aid from social agencies.

The second and probably more important way to help such patients is to work with them in an attempt to discover why the particular situation has produced such an abnormal depression. Since many persons have lost their jobs, many have been "stood up," and many have lost their possessions through fire, why, then, should one person become pathologically depressed when the rest do not? The situation must have been especially significant—*traumatic*—for the patient and might be meaningful to him in several ways. The trauma may be rooted in the past experience of the patient, even in his earliest childhood: for example, as a child of six he may have gone through the frightening experience of having seen his house burn down. Should the experience be repeated when he is grown up, the patient remembers how he felt as a child and how his parents reacted, that everything was confused, and everyone in a state of emotional turmoil, that what used to be his bed could no longer be his bed—that everything in his world, in fact, was topsy-turvy. Although he may have successfully recovered from this experience when he was six, if, as a married man with a family, he should again lose his home through fire, the previous trauma makes his adult loss have a very special significance for him. The psychiatrist, therefore, must help him cope with the reactive depression produced by this individually unique experience.

Psychotherapy, the treatment used in such cases, is designed to give the patient knowledge or insight into the reasons for his condition and in this manner help him find relief. Psychotherapy is of additional value in that it serves as a preventative or prophylactic measure, because experiences with special significance for an individual at one time will affect him the same way in the future. A man who responds to being jilted by going into a reactive depression will react the same way to every similar future situation, and will continue to do so unless a psychiatrist can help him solve his problem or emotional complex. Temporary relief may frequently be obtained by the use of anti-depressant drugs, such as the amphetamines, which produce a sense of euphoria and thus tend to counteract the gloomy outlook so characteristic of the patient with a reactive depression. Similarly, minor tranquilizers, such as Miltown® and Equanil® (meprobamate), Librium® (chlordiazepoxide hydrochloride), Valium® (diazepam), etc., may prove helpful in reducing the mild agitation and uneasiness which may accompany the depression.

Prognosis in such cases is excellent. Most reactive depressions are minor in degree and self-limited; they are normal reactions, and people recover from them without needing any help at all; of the people who do go into a severe neurotic reactive depression and come to the psychiatrist for help, almost all can be helped, in terms of the immediate situation as well as of their emotional condition. Very rarely does a patient with a reactive depression become so severely depressed that electro-shock treatment is required. Usually, psychotherapy with or without chemotherapy will suffice.

The next illness in the neurotic affective group is known as *delayed grief reaction*, a depression, with or without various other symptoms, which comes on after a lapse of time in response to the death of a loved person. The patients feel sad and depressed, weep and lament, and sometimes, but not always, experience hallucinations, delusions, anxiety, physical complaints, etc. The illness begins after a delay of six months or longer following the loss of a beloved parent, sibling, child, marital partner, friend, or other individual.

A very interesting history attaches to this condition. It begins in 1917 with Freud's article, *Mourning and Melancholia*, in which he studied the psychological processes going on in the normal person who has suffered the loss of a loved one. After the death of the loved person, he discovered, comes a period of grief in which the individual cries, wails and generally feels extremely depressed; and such grief consumes a great deal of energy. Freud noticed that next follows a period of praise of the dead person. This human phenomenon is so general that everyone can be said to become a saint at death's door—that, indeed, no one bad has ever died. A mother who was a social butterfly and paid no attention to her children may be praised after her death as an ideal parent; or a father who was a hopeless alcoholic may be praised as a wonderful provider. The final stage in the reaction to the death is for the remaining family to forgive themselves. The children begin to say: "When mother was ill, we had the best doctors and nurses available. We brought her presents and gave all of our evenings so that we could be with her." They are forgiving themselves by saying, in essence: "*We* did not want her to die. *We* did everything we could to prevent it." Thus, the family tends to handle and relieve its guilt. Such processes are part of normal mourning.

Another phase of this research was stimulated by Erich Lindemann, a Boston psychiatrist, who used the horrible experience of the Coconut Grove fire to study the causes of delayed grief reaction. On a broad scale, similar observations were made during the second World War in the U.S. Air Force. The flight crew of each bomber, it became evident, is really one big family. The pilot of the plane—the "daddy-pilot," to use a highly descriptive phrase—is like a father to the other members of the crew, who depend on him to bring the plane safely back, much the same as children depend on *their* "daddies" to support them. The co-pilot is like the mother in a family, while the navigator, tail-gunner, bombardier, etc. represent the children. The Air Force recognizes that this group comprises a "family" in a realistic psychological sense, and tries to keep each crew together, as if trying to maintain the unity of a family. Each crew member comes to feel that he belongs to all the other members of his crew or "family." If the "daddy-pilot" was killed, one of the remaining crew members might become depressed within six months or a year, exhibiting a delayed grief reaction. Further investigation showed that, at the time of the pilot's death, the now-depressed crew member had been unable to feel grief. Many such crew members said: "I should have cried, but the tears wouldn't come. It was as if I had an iceberg inside me, or as if my heart had turned to stone." Perhaps the most characteristic aspect of a delayed grief reaction is just this immediate reaction of coldness, of inability to express feelings which will burst forth uncontrollably at a later time.

Another Bostonian, Joshua Loth Liebman, deserves credit

for a third phase in the history of this research. Rabbi Liebman's famous book, *Peace of Mind,* contains a section on
death in which he points out that it is perfectly all right
to be sad when a beloved person dies, and that the rituals of
all faiths recognize that, at the time of death, survivors are
supposed to grieve, that people need not be ashamed of
weeping for the dead. Simple and obvious as this observation
may seem, it had a tremendous impact on a world which was
growing so callous that people often buried a loved person
one day and were out having a good time the next. Rabbi
Liebman brought to popular attention the fact that failure
to grieve can lead to serious emotional trouble.

In the etiology of delayed grief reaction, death of a loved
individual constitutes one factor; the second factor is the
person who suffers that loss, the patient. It is necessary to
discover what kept him from reacting as he should have at
the time of death. If he was tail-gunner of an Air Force
flight crew, why didn't he weep when his "daddy-pilot" was
killed? In almost every such case the answer is that the
patient had ambivalent feelings toward the departed, which
means that he felt two opposite emotions at once, such as
love and hate. If the patient's Oedipus complex shows unresolved ambivalent feelings toward his father, and if in later
life as a tail-gunner he had ambivalent feelings toward his
pilot, the latter's death would certainly have a special significance for and a special effect upon him. His feelings of love
would leave him sad and sorry at the loss of this loved person;
but his negative feelings of hatred would constitute a real
problem for him. An excellent example of such negative
feelings occurs in the opera Hansel and Gretel, when the
two children dance around the oven in which the witch is
cooking, and happily sing: "Ha, ha, the wicked witch is
dead." What they have hoped and wished for has taken
place, so their negative feelings are fulfilled. Since the negative part of the tail-gunner's ambivalent feelings toward the

pilot made him feel happy at the death, it was obviously impossible for him to feel sad or grieve.

Psychotherapy is the treatment for this illness. Since there is no way for the psychiatrist to bring the dead back to life, he must try to help the patient handle the ambivalent feelings more successfully. This is accomplished by helping the patient gain insight into his negative feelings. The patient must have someone—here, the therapist—toward whom he can feel and express his emotions. When in therapy an emotion is transferred from a situation or person to the therapist, the term *transference* is used. It is by transference that feelings originally felt towards the patient's father and later toward the "daddy-pilot" begin to be expressed toward the therapist. In delayed grief reaction, the patient develops a transference toward his doctor which contains ambivalent feelings of love and hate. Although the therapist does nothing to deserve the hate or anything particular to deserve the love, it is a function of the patient's neurosis to transpose the feelings onto the doctor, who may then point out these feelings to the patient. He then asks him such questions as "Why do you hate me?" or "Why do you love me?" The psychiatrist would then remark, "These feelings must go back to the way you felt toward someone earlier in your life." The patient eventually becomes aware of the fact that he once had such feelings toward his father. The therapist's second objective is to help straighten out the patient's feelings by not acting as the latter's father had done. Obviously, there had been a reason for the original ambivalent feelings toward the father. Perhaps the father's attitude toward the patient swung rapidly from hot to cold, or he was cruel and abusive to him, or treated him like a baby or a girl—there are many possibilities. The therapist must not act as the father did, must not repeat the unfortunate pattern of the patient's relationship with his father; indeed, within certain limits, he should strive to be the exact opposite of the father. Treatment thus can be an emotional re-education which grants the patient a second chance to achieve a healthy emotional adjustment. Being in the same situation again, the patient is treated so that he feels differently and can handle himself and the situation differently. Psychotherapy, carried on to achieve insight into emotions, is a very rewarding procedure for dealing with cases of delayed grief reaction.

Prognosis is excellent; practically all of these patients recover. Furthermore, the therapy is prophylactic in that the patients are kept from future abnormal reactions to the deaths of people of equal and similar importance to them.

RECOMMENDED READING

For complete bibliographic data, see also the General Bibliography following the Preface.

Abraham: *Selected Papers*, pp. 137-156, 418-479.
Fenichel: *Psychoanalytic Theory of Neurosis,* chapter 17.
Freud: Mourning and Melancholia. *The Standard Edition,* Volume 14, pp. 237-260.
Grinker, R. R., and Spiegel, J. P. *Men Under Stress.* New York: The Blakiston Division, 1945, chapter 12. Available in paperback: McGraw-Hill Book Co., 1963.
Hoch, P. H., and Zubin, J. *Depression.* New York: Grune & Stratton, 1954, chapters, 7, 8, 10, 15, and 16.
Liebman, J. L. *Peace of Mind.* New York: Simon & Schuster, 1946.
Lindemann, E. "The Symptomatology and Management of Acute Grief." *American Journal of Psychiatry,* 1944, *101*: 141-148.
Ludwig, A. O. "Neuroses Occurring in Soldiers after Prolonged Combat Exposure." *Bulletin of the Menninger Clinic,* 1947, *11*: 15-23.
Mezer, R. R., and Rheingold, P. D. "Mental Capacity and Incompetency: A Psycho-Legal Problem." *American Journal of Psychiatry, 118*: 827-831, March, 1962.
Solomon, H. C., and Yakovlev, P. I. *Manual of Military Neuropsychiatry.* Philadelphia: W. B. Saunders, 1944, pp. 527, 535-537.

CHAPTER 10

Personality Disorders

Patients with personality disorders suffer from a defect in the superego. Because of this imperfection, these patients cause society to suffer or cause themselves to suffer. They exhibit lifelong patterns of maladaptive behavior. The second edition of the *Diagnostic and Statistical Manual of Mental Disorders* lists nine different types of personality disorders together with problems of sexual deviation, alcoholism, and drug dependence.

The antisocial personality[1] shows difficulties in his adjustment to life from an early age. During the oral period he may display feeding problems, perhaps by holding food in his mouth and then spitting it out at his parents. He has difficulties in bowel training during the anal stage. About the age of three, he becomes a "problem child" who may show aggressive behavior by kicking his parents in the shins, spitting at them or calling them nasty names; or, the behavior problem may be refusing to obey orders, lying, stealing or having temper tantrums, etc. When he enters school about the age of five or six, he becomes a problem, not in terms of

---

[1] *Antisocial personality* is the diagnostic term for persons who commit antisocial and criminal acts. "Psychopathic personality" and "sociopathic personality" were the old terms for this group of illnesses.

his intellectual capacities, but rather in his behavior and
general adjustment to the school situation. Such children are
frequently truant. They will hitch rides on trolley cars and
trucks, trying to get something for nothing. In early adolescence, they gather in their characteristic gangs, and
juvenile delinquency begins; these gangs raid the fruitstand,
break into the corner drugstore, steal things from the five-
and-ten store, learn to gamble, play pool, and swear. In
mid-adolescence, around the age of fourteen to sixteen, they
become sexually active in a promiscuous and anti-social
fashion, and in later adolescence begin to indulge in larceny,
breaking and entering, assault and battery, forgery, murder,
rape, and robbery. By then, they are fully equipped for the
reform schools, jails and penal institutions which society
says they will inhabit periodically for the rest of their lives.

The antisocial personality, usually established in the
first few years of life, may become a permanent way of life
for the individual. In a certain number of cases, the drive
toward antisocial activity seems to die out in the mid-thirties
or early forties; successful parole cases may well fall into
this so-called "burned out" group.

The etiology of the antisocial personality derives from
the fact that the superego is either underdeveloped or malformed. It will be recalled that the superego is formed, first,
from the bowel-training of the anal period, and secondly,
when, during the solution of the Oedipus complex, the
individual identifies with the parent of the same sex. In these
patients something has gone wrong in one or both of these
processes. The superego may be underdeveloped or weak
because of failure to form a strong identification during the
solution of the Oedipus complex and/or because of too
lenient and inattentive bowel training. The superego may
be malformed if the individual has identified with an unsat-
isfactory and socially unacceptable object; antisocial person-

alities are frequently found to come from home environments where there has been obvious antisocial activity by the father and/or mother. It would thus almost seem to be a hereditary disease. Treating individuals with antisocial personalities poses some very serious problems. Putting them into penal institutions serves temporarily to relieve society of their misdeeds. This seldom changes the person who characteristically does not learn from experience, for to do so would require a well-functioning superego. Punishment for his crime accomplishes little. If an individual is to feel guilty—and the feeling of guilt is a prerequisite for any change in behavior—his superego must be fully developed; all the antisocial personality can feel guilty about is that he was caught, not that he has committed a crime. In some cases, the delinquency or antisocial behavior may represent an attempt at solving internal or external problems, and these cases frequently may be helped by psychotherapy.

Many agencies are trying to transform individuals with antisocial personalities into socially acceptable individuals by such sociological reforms, as cleaning up the slums, rebuilding the tenement areas, promoting the Big Brother movement, forming clubs where adolescent boys and girls can put their energy to socially acceptable purposes, etc. The effectiveness of these sociological reforms is still unknown.

The prognosis of individuals with antisocial personalities, obviously, is poor, except for the fact that many do "burn out" in their middle thirties and early forties.

The *passive-dependent* type of personality disorder may be likened to a baby nursing at its mother's breast or a child afraid to leave her apron strings. The perfect example of a person with a passive-dependent type of personality disorder is Casper Milquetoast. Such a person fears his own shadow, is hen-pecked, dares not ask the boss for a raise, does as he is told without questioning, and, to his own detriment, holds himself back from any aggressive or independent action. This passive-dependent personality raises tremendous demands for satisfaction of dependency strivings and is frequently found in alcoholics. However, it must be remembered that passivity and dependency exist to a slight degree in every normal person.

The *obsessive compulsive* personality is overly clean, neat, punctual, stingy, miserly, stubborn, pedantic, and meticulous. Again, these traits exist in most normal people to a moderate degree, but in the obsessive compulsive they are in such excess that they become a detriment. His personality is rigid, unbending and honest to a fault; he has excessive concerns with conscience; he makes tremendous demands upon himself and is unable to let go or to relax.

The *hysterical* personality disorder tends to sexualize everything and genitalize nothing. Since such individuals see being sexual as a way of life, they act seductively and in their conversation make repeated references to sexual matters. Yet, despite this surface sexual behavior and speech, they only talk a good game, for their actual genital adjustments are always poor. The male hysteric is sometimes called the Don Juan character, and colloquially is known as a wolf. He stands on the street corner, whistles at passing girls, cuts a striking and dramatic figure on the dance floor by wooing and impressing as many girls as he possibly can in an evening, and is an expert at making love in automobiles. He rarely marries and, even if he does, normal genital activity is not for him; he must constantly prove his masculinity by seducing every woman, for he sees them all as a challenge and an opportunity to prove himself. The female with an hysterical personality disorder indulges in the same type of activity with men as the male does with women, so that sexual intercourse, whether in or outside of marriage, never satisfies her; she must repeatedly entice and seduce men to prove to herself her femininity. The irony lies in the fact that she is never satisfied, never proves her femininity to herself, and never achieves a true genital adjustment. In other cases of hysterical personality, the attention-seeking, self-dramatizing, oversensitivity, and emotional instability are expressed in nonsexual areas and ways of living.

The etiology of hysterical types of personality disorder lies in some defect in superego formation; in practically every case the defect is qualitative as well as quantitative. In this personality disorder the superego seems to be overdeveloped, for it exerts such a powerful influence in molding the personality that it seems wholly dominant. It is as if the individual had to act in every situation in accordance with the dictates of this malformed, overdeveloped superego, despite his own needs, desires, or id impulses.

Individuals with hysterical personalities cause themselves to suffer, are aware of it and seek help. Therapy of this illness falls properly to the psychiatrist. The key frequently lies in the therapeutic transference situation by which that which has gone before and caused the superego malformation can be corrected. Women suffering from hysterical personality disorders, one of the most frequent illnesses seen by the psychiatrist in the out-patient clinic or private office, usually develop a transference in which they try to seduce the doctor. With the help of the therapist who points out her behavior to her, she becomes aware of what she is trying to do, and then both undertake the task of unearthing the origin of her difficulty. It usually stems from an unresolved Oedipus complex in which the girl has never come to face the reality that she cannot have her father as a sexual partner. She has grown convinced that this is a definite possibility and has then set out to prove to herself that not only can she get her father but any, indeed every, man. So she is at first convinced that the therapist, who ideally ought to be a man, will not be immune to her attempts. As she gains insight into the origin of her difficulty, the patient will eventually face the reality that intercourse with her father is not possible for her, and will give up her seductive, promiscuous, ungratifying behavior.

The prognosis for individuals with hysterical types of personality disorder in psychotherapy is quite favorable. In these conditions, psychotherapy, aiming at insight and utilizing transference phenomena, is the treatment of choice —as a matter of fact, the *only* treatment. Nothing else will work—not even drugs.

To understand the *sexual deviations,* it is necessary first to discuss the sexual instinct, which like all instincts has both an aim and an object. The aim of any instinct is the act which satisfies it, and its object is the thing which satisfies it. The instinct of hunger has as its aim the act of eating, and as its object, food. The aim of the sexual instinct is intercourse, either at once or at some future time, and its object is an adult person of the opposite sex.

Abnormalities involving the *object* of the sexual instinct are called *inversions;* the most common of these is homosexuality in which an individual of the same sex is chosen as the sexual object. Obviously, the reference here is to homosexuality as a way of life, not to the sporadic homosexual episodes that occur in adolescence. Another inversion is called bestiality in which an animal is chosen as the object of the sexual instinct. A third example is the choice of children as objects instead of adults, which is called *pedophilia.*

Deviations in the *aim* of the sexual instinct are called *perversions.* They can be divided into substitutes for the normal aim and into exaggerations of some of the subsidiary aspects of sexual intercourse. Among the substitute aims are found the acts of fellatio (inserting the penis in the mouth instead of in the vagina) and cunnilingus (placing the tongue instead of the penis in the vagina). These are termed perversions when they completely overshadow the normal aim of the sexual instinct, namely, sexual intercourse.

Perversions due to the exaggeration of subsidiary aspects are masochism and sadism, and voyeurism and exhibitionism. A normal part of the act of sexual intercourse is defloration of the woman by the man; and in subsequent sexual intercourse she is hugged, squeezed, and lain upon by the man. All these acts imply some pain, hurt, or suffering imposed on her by him. When these partial, secondary, and subsidiary aspects of sexual intercourse are exaggerated to the extent that they become the primary aspects of the sexual instinct, completely supplanting the act of sexual intercourse, the perversions of masochism and sadism result. Masochism means to receive pleasure from being hurt, and sadism means receiving pleasure from hurting someone else. There exist entire societies of masochists and sadists who indulge in sadomasochistic orgies of beating and being beaten, of whipping and being whipped, etc. The perversion of sexual masochism often extends over the rest of the individual's personality, producing a masochistic personality disorder in which the individual suffers himself to be hurt, degraded, embarrassed, rejected and humiliated, and adopts this as his way of life. Sadists, too, can form a sadistic character structure.

In the normal act of sexual intercourse, it is pleasing for the partners to look upon each other, the woman usually liking to be looked upon by the man, who enjoys looking upon her. When these normal but subsidiary parts of intercourse become so exaggerated that they completely supplant the normal aim of the sexual instinct, the intercourse itself, the perversions of voyeurism and exhibitionism result. Voyeurism is defined as pleasure from looking at others, and exhibitionism as pleasure from exhibiting oneself. Characteristic voyeurs, colloquially called Peeping Toms, satisfy their sexual instincts by looking instead of by the act of sexual intercourse, and it is literally the act of looking, not anything they see, which gratifies them. An important part of this perversion is the excitement of doing the forbidden, taking a chance on being discovered, etc. The exhibitionist, who seeks out secluded areas as exist, for instance, in subway stations, gratifies his sexual instinct by exhibiting himself to a passing woman, and his satisfaction or thrill usually depends on her reaction. In order to feel gratified, he must evoke in the woman the reaction of fear, horror, amazement, wonder, envy or surprise; if she says nonchalantly, "Oh, put that away," he gets no thrill. Female voyeurs are quite rare, but female exhibitionists are common. The burlesque queen, the artist's model, and women who dress in revealing gowns and scanty bathing suits may well include in their numbers many exhibitionists, if an exhibitionist is defined as one who obtains sexual gratification through the act of exhibiting and not at all through intercourse.

The dynamics of the sexual deviations are best understood in terms of the concept of *acting out*. This is an ego defense mechanism, a way of solving conflicts by expressing them in actions which themselves become a way of life. The ego, for example, can act out id impulses. These impulse-ridden personalities "can resist everything but temptation" because the superego is too weak to quell the desires or demands of the id. In other cases, the superego constellation exerts a compelling force on the ego; the ego acts out the superego's dictates and loses sight completely of the reality situation and of the individual's real internal needs, so that needs and wants become confused. The ego then adopts this superego-dominated mode of action as a way of life. The process of acting out conflicts is frequently seen in conjunction with other psychoses or neuroses, and is certainly also a major part of normal living; normal people, however, act out only what is realistic and socially acceptable.

In dealing with patients who act out, the psychiatrist must show himself so completely non-judgmental and uncritical of the patient that the patient will allow himself to be understood by the therapist; it is only by understanding these patients and by helping them to understand themselves that the psychiatrist can help them to a happier adjustment in life. Many homosexuals, male as well as female, can be helped to a heterosexual adjustment in life. It may be well to note here that courts are adopting a more therapeutic orientation toward problems of this type.

The problems associated with drug dependence and alcoholism are multiple. The addictive personality tends to be immature, dependent, demanding, compulsive, unrealistic, and insatiable. Many of the drugs on which the individual is dependent have effects of their own that further complicate the clinical picture. Alcohol and opiates, for example, have withdrawal effects; LSD may have delayed reactions and may even influence future generations by damaging chromosomes. Marijuana has no addictive properties of its own, but may lead the user into groups dealing with other drugs, some of which are addictive. There are some legitimate medical uses for some of these drugs, but there are serious and severe legal penalties associated with the abuse and nonmedical use of these drugs. The alcoholic and the drug-dependent persons therefore, have serious social, legal, medical, familial, psychiatric, and personal problems.

The treatment of alcoholism and drug dependence is difficult. The acute alcoholic needs expert medical attention in order to detoxify him, and Antabuse® (disulfiram), Alcoholics Anonymous, and psychotherapy may be of help in keeping the chronic alcoholic sober. Methadone may be helpful in opiate addiction, but hospitalization is almost always necessary to help the addict break the habit. Prolonged hospitalization, phenothiazine medications, and intensive psychotherapy may be required in the rehabilitation of individuals who suffer from psychoses associated with meth-edrine ("speed"), marijuana ("pot"), LSD, and other hallu-cinogenic and psychedelic drugs.

RECOMMENDED READING

For complete bibliographic data, see also the General Bibliography following the Preface.

Aichhorn, A. *Wayward Youth.* New York: Viking Press, 1965. (Paper-back edition).

Banay, R. S. *We Call Them Criminals.* New York: Appleton-Century-Crofts, 1957.

Batchelor: *Henderson and Gillespie's Textbook of Psychiatry,* chapters 9 and 13.

Cleckley, H. M. *Mask of Sanity,* Fourth edition. St. Louis: Mosby, 1964.

Ewalt and Farnsworth: *Textbook of Psychiatry,* chapters 10-14.

Fenichel: *The Psychoanalytic Theory of Neurosis,* chapters 16 and 20.

Freud: Some Character Types Met With in Psychoanalytic Work. *The Standard Edition,* Volume 14, pp. 332-336.

Glueck, S., and Glueck, E. *Unraveling Juvenile Delinquency.* Cam-bridge: Harvard University Press, 1950.

Guttmacher, M. S., and Weihofen, H. *Psychiatry and the Law.* New York: W. W. Norton, 1952.

Hoch, P. H., and Zubin, J. *Psychiatry and the Law.* New York: Grune & Stratton, 1955.

Kolb: *Noyes' Modern Clinical Psychiatry,* chapters 29 and 30.

Mezer, R. R., and Blotner, H. "Alcoholism." In *Traumatic Medicine and Surgery for the Attorney,* Volume 7, pp. 505-527. Washington, D.C.: Butterworth, Inc., 1962.

CHAPTER 11

Neuroses and Psychophysiological Disorders

Since *neurosis* and *psychoneurosis* are synonymous terms, they can be used interchangeably. A neurosis is characterized by the presence of anxiety. It is always due to emotional conflicts early in life, and specifically involving unresolved feelings occurring during the Oedipus complex—the Oedipal feelings having been repressed into the unconscious, so that the neurotic difficulty is precipitated by re-enactment of the original emotional conflict. For example, a boy who does not lose his hostility toward an overly dominating father through the process of identification is left with an unresolved emotional conflict. If, in an attempt to solve it, his ego chooses the mechanism of repression, the emotional conflict will exist in his unconscious under pressure and in a state of suspended animation. The repression may occur at the age of six, and at eighteen the young man may find himself a private in the Army under the command of a master sergeant who acts in a dominating fashion as the boy's father had done. This may strike a note in tune with the boy's repressed Oedipal conflict, cause re-enactment of the original situation and precipitate a neurotic difficulty. Similarly, a girl who does not solve her hostile or ambivalent feelings toward her mother during the Oedipal stage will repress them; later in life, as a student nurse being taught and supervised by a head nurse, she too may find herself in a re-enactment of this original situation. Since her feelings in the new situation correspond to those originally repressed, a neurotic difficulty may be precipitated.

While neuroses are characterized by a number of positive features, it is the lack of certain features which differentiates neuroses from all other personality and emotional difficulties and permits psychiatrists to make a differential diagnosis. A first negative feature is the absence of *etiologically significant* organic pathology. Although a neurotic, like anyone else, can have organic pathology, it cannot be of etiological significance in the neurotic symptoms. A neurotic may have a pain in the back and have unrelated organic pathology, but his pain is neurotic only if no relation to organic pathology exists.

A second negative feature of neurosis is absence of mental deficiency. Neurotic individuals are not stupid but rather are as intelligent as, or more intelligent than, normal persons. Many psychiatrists feel that a mentally deficient individual is not intelligent enough to develop a neurosis; they state flatly that neuroses and mental deficiency cannot coexist in the same person. A third feature that neurotics lack is the loss of the sense of reality; in neurotics the sense of reality is intact, if somewhat distorted. In this fashion, psychiatrists differentiate neuroses from the psychoses of schizophrenia, manic-depressive psychosis, involutional melancholia, involutional psychosis of the paranoid type, psychosis with organic brain disease, etc. Fourth comes the absence of primary mood pathology, which is present in involutional melancholia and manic-depressive psychosis; included, however, in the neurotic group are the affective illnesses in which the mood

pathology is secondary, such as reactive depression and delayed grief reaction already described in Chapter 9.

Diagnosis of neurosis is made by determining first the
lack of these four features and then the presence of one or
more of the positive features that divide the neuroses into
several sub-groups. A diagnosis of neurosis can never be made
solely on the basis of exclusion but requires proving that at
least one of the positive features is present.

The positive features define the ways in which an individual can be neurotic; all are based on various mechanisms
of defense which the ego may use, or finds necessary to use,
when the repressed Oedipal conflict is re-enacted. The first
sub-group of the neuroses is, generally speaking, characterized by ego defense mechanisms in which the individual loses
control of emergency mechanisms in the body. The "old
school" of psychiatry used to call these *true* or *real* neuroses.
The two main emergency mechanisms in the body are fear
and tiredness. Fear is activated when a person finds him-
selp in a threatening or dangerous situation;[1] it is a normal
response which prepares the body for "fight or flight." Everyone has experienced fear at one time or another—when nearly
involved in an automobile accident, on the verge of being
assaulted, when an animal has threatened to attack, when
startled by an unexpected noise, when suddenly disturbed
from deep concentration, or in some similar case. A normal
feeling of fear is always associated with physiological phenomena connected with the autonomic nervous system, such as
rapid heart beat (tachycardia), palpitation, perspiration, gid-
diness or feeling of faintness, a sensation of "butterflies in the
stomach," a weak-kneed feeling, a desire to urinate, a prickly

---

[1] See page 103 for discussion of traumatic situations in reactive depressions. "Traumatic neuroses" are those in which the ego is unable
to deal successfully with emotions so that it is in danger of losing its
mastery over the emotional life of the individual. In this sense, every
neurosis is a traumatic one, and neurotic defenses are called forth in an
attempt at self-preservation to maintain homeostasis.

feeling of the skin as if the hair were standing on end, and a sharp inspiration of air followed by a momentary cessation of breathing and then by hyperventilation.

An *anxiety neurosis* is characterized by the presence of anxiety, and anxiety is defined as fear without an object or a cause. Individuals with anxiety neurosis lose control of the normal emergency mechanism of fear, so that they experience fear and its physiological concomitants in situations in which normal persons see no reason for and do not experience fear. The anxiety in this neurosis may be constant and low grade, may occur in acute episodes called *panics,* or may be a combination so that the neurotic experiences a low level of chronic anxiety to which are added acute exacerbations in the form of panics. The etiology of anxiety neurosis is known. The first cause is the unsolved Oedipus complex, with unresolved and repressed emotions[2] that create tension. Second is the re-enactment of this original conflict, intensifying the originally repressed emotions to the point that the ego can no longer handle them but must find a new way of dealing with these feelings. In an anxiety neurosis, the ego loses control of the normal emergency mechanism of fear as an attempt at solving, or defending itself against, the feelings aroused by the precipitating or traumatic situation.

The treatment of anxiety neurosis is psychotherapy or psychoanalysis. In therapy, after first telling his symptoms, which are indeed very troublesome to him, the patient begins to develop a transference toward the therapist, consisting of the unsolved aspect of the Oedipus complex, of those unresolved feelings which have been repressed and subsequently reawakened in the re-enactment precipitating the neurotic difficulty. As the patient gains insight into the emotional conflict underlying his symptoms and as he experiences an emotional re-education during which he has a new chance to

[2] The castration complex is a frequent etiological factor in anxiety neuroses.

solve these feelings correctly, his symptoms gradually diminish and subside. Such individuals benefit further from psychotherapy in that they achieve a more mature type of personality. Although the results of therapy in treating anxiety
neurosis are excellent, it is unfortunately true—and this is
so for all neuroses—that no adequate statistical studies have
been made, mainly because the patients are ambulatory,
make up the everyday working population, and are treated
in psychiatric out-patient departments or in the private
offices of psychiatrists. Various major and minor tranquilizers
may also be used to make the patient more comfortable or to
increase his ability to work psychotherapeutically on his underlying problems. Psychotherapy and psychoanalysis can and
do discover and correct the cause of anxiety neuroses.

The body's second normal emergency mechanism, tiredness or fatigue, appears after exertion and before exhaustion.
Everyone has experienced a normal feeling of tiredness after
exceptionally hard physical or mental work, after going without the usual amount of sleep, when physically ill, or
after subjecting the body to unusual strain. This normal
emergency mechanism of tiredness or fatigue warns the body
that exhaustion will follow if the exertion continues. *Neurasthenia,* the neurotic illness in which control is lost over
the normal emergency mechanism of tiredness, has as its
main symptom tiredness or fatigue without apparent cause.
Neurasthenic individuals feel tired and fatigued even when
they have not over-exerted themselves—often, indeed, when
they have not exerted themselves in the slightest and when
they have not lost any sleep; their fatigue occurs in situations which do not produce tiredness in normal individuals.
Besides the important primary symptom of fatigue, the
characteristic clinical picture of neurasthenia often includes
gastrointestinal symptoms, such as belching, rumblings in

the stomach, and flatus (passing gas through the rectum), as well as migratory aches and pains involving all parts of the body. Other characteristic symptoms of neurasthenia are debility, lassitude, a feeling of weakness, and loss of pep, energy, and ambition—all without any assignable reason. Seldom, if ever, do neurasthenics experience exactly the same complaint twice in succession. Neurasthenia and hypochondriasis are closely related.

Both etiology and therapy of this condition are somewhat vague. Although in psychotherapy or psychoanalysis, neurasthenics, like other patients, begin by telling their complaints, the psychiatrist soon becomes aware that they continue to recite their complaints. A neurasthenic may stick to his recital of complaints of tiredness, debility, aches in the stomach or head, etc., to the extent that the psychiatrist may never hear about a mother or father for whom the patient has feelings. Thus, the treatment of neurasthenia may not work out in the same way as that of anxiety neurosis. Many neurasthenics are constant visitors to the medical out-patient departments and to the private offices of general practitioners where they may be given vitamin B injections, liver and iron pills, tranquilizers or energizers, physiotherapy, a pat on the back, or a word of sympathy and two words of encouragement. Psychiatrists are resigned to this state of affairs, because, much to their regret, they have as yet nothing to offer many of these patients. A good deal of theoretical speculation has attempted to explain why some neurasthenics elude and evade the usual course of the neurotic patient in therapy; one theory postulates that the symptoms are so meaningful and important that the patient cannot develop the type of transference necessary for effective therapy.

The second sub-group of neuroses is called *psychasthenia,*

in the terminology of the "old school." Neuroses in this group make use of defense mechanisms which are described as *anankastic;* the term, deriving from the Greek, means involuntary and designates something that forces itself upon the patient against his will. Anankastic defenses are used either indirectly in warding off the anxiety of an anxiety neurosis, or directly when the ego is unable to cope with the combination of originally repressed conflict and its subsequent re-enactment. There are three anankastic defenses, and consequently three symptoms and three different neuroses are found in the sub-group psychasthenia. A *phobic neurosis* is characterized by the presence of phobias, or anankastic fears, which include unwarranted fear of heights, fear of dark places, fear of open spaces, fear of being enclosed, fear of crowds, fear of locomotives, fear of snakes, fear of being alone, and so forth. Some of these fears are familiar to everyone; the differentiation between a normal and a neurotic phobia is based on the degree to which the symptom interferes with total adjustment; for example, if a person's fear is so intense that he will not leave the house, will not go to school, will not work, in short, will not function normally in society, he exhibits a neurotic phobia. Small, subsidiary phobias are called normal because they do not interfere with the total adjustment to life.

An obsessive or *obsessional neurosis* is characterized by the presence of obsessions, which are anankastic thoughts or ideas. As a phobic neurotic has fears which intrude against his will, so an individual with an obsessional neurosis has recurring thoughts or ideas intruding into his personality against his will. An obsessional idea frequently includes the thought of some future act and involves hostility; typically, a woman might be obsessed with the idea that she is going to kill her child. Normal thoughts may be called obsessional if they intrude into the mind against the will; if they do not interfere with overall adjustment or functioning, they are normal. A neurotic obsessional thought, however, is so recurrent that it does interfere with adjustment and functioning capacity. A person suffering from obsessive neurosis gets so involved in thinking obsessional thoughts that he cannot work, go to school, or be at all happy in life. It is also important to distinguish neurotic obsessions from schizophrenic delusions which are much farther removed from normality. The difference is the same as that between a thought or idea (the obsession) and a belief (the delusion).

A *compulsive neurosis* is characterized by the presence of compulsions, or anankastic acts, which intrude upon an individual's personality against his will. Having to tie, untie and retie one's shoelaces over and over again; spending hours washing one's hands; having to count to three once, then three times and then to repeat the whole process again; having to walk around a chair seven times before taking a seat; spending hours each day checking and rechecking door locks, the lock on the car or the gas jets of the stove, all these are typical anankastic acts typical of compulsive neurosis. Here, again, neurotic compulsions must be differentiated from the normal ones which are a part of every personality. Most people make getting up in the morning and going to bed at night a kind of ritual; some have to step on every crack in the sidewalk and others have to avoid every crack. These behaviors are normal because they do not interfere with adjustment to life and some might even be useful. The individual with a neurotic compulsion, however, has to spend most of his time washing his hands or stepping on cracks in the sidewalk, so that these activities interfere with his normal adjustment and functioning capacities. Very often patients combine in varying degrees both obsessional and compulsive symptoms; they are then said to have an obsessive-compulsive neurosis. The etiology of phobic, obsessional and compulsive neuroses is well authenticated. In phobic neurosis the mechanism of defense is displacement. The ego keeps the same feeling but changes the object. For example, instead of fearing his father or a master sergeant in a re-enactment of the Oedipal situation, a private in the Army might displace his fear on to horses, and develop a phobia for horses. This displacement may solve his problem with the master sergeant but will create an incapacitating phobia in regard to horses.

The etiology of obsessional neurosis involves the ego defense mechanism of isolation which, theoretically, consists in isolating a complex from the main currents and streams of the personality—making it *ego-alien*. Theory postulates that the bundle or complex of feeling, from its ego-alien position, sends impulses back into the stream of consciousness that constitute or provoke obsessional thoughts. Since the complex that is isolated very often consists of a phobia, it is no surprise that the history of obsessional neurosis frequently shows a phobic neurosis preceding the onset of the obsessional neurosis.

The etiology of compulsive neurosis involves the ego mechanism of undoing in which the compulsive act is an attempt to undo the obsessional thought. Thus, beneath the surface symptom of compulsion, there is usually an obsessional thought: the compulsive act of handwashing might be an attempt to undo the thought of guilt or sin—as in Lady Macbeth's washing of her hands, symbolizing an attempt to cleanse herself of the sin of murder. If a woman has the obsessional thought that she might kill her child, her compulsive attempt to undo this thought could be to keep all the kitchen knives hidden, or to check the gas range repeatedly. Another aspect of obsessional and com-

pulsive neuroses is that, characteristically, not only the
Oedipus complex is involved in their etiology but also the
preceding difficulties of the anal period. Such neurotics are,
therefore, more complicated and sicker than phobic individuals whose difficulty appears to lie primarily in the
Oedipal (genital) stage of development.

Treatment of these illnesses becomes progressively more
difficult as one goes from phobic through obsessional to
compulsive neurosis. Treatment of phobic neurosis involves
insight psychotherapy or psychoanalysis, and the patient
usually sustains an excellent result from therapy. In the
case of obsessional neurosis, therapy tends to be a good
deal more difficult, lengthy and intensive. With compulsive
neurosis, psychotherapy may be of help, but prolonged and
intensive psychoanalytic therapy may be indicated. It is not
yet clear what contribution chemotherapy can make to
the treatment of these illnesses.

The third and final sub-group of the neuroses, and the
third and final of the positive features which characterize
neuroses, is called *hysterical neurosis*.[3] In this group the ego
uses the defense mechanism of conversion, in which emotional conflicts are converted or transformed so that they
exert a physical effect upon the body. When the original,
now repressed Oedipal conflict is re-enacted, the combination
of the feelings from the past with those of the present may
be too much for the ego to master, whereupon it may use
the defense mechanism of conversion; or the ego may call
into play a conversion mechanism in an attempt to ward off
and handle differently the unpleasant feelings of anxiety
neurosis. Since the hysterical neuroses show emotional conflict transformed into an influence on the body, the clinical

[3] The term *hysteria* derives from the Greek word for womb; it used to be
thought that the organ involved in conversion neurosis was afflicted by the
womb's moving to a new area of the body, for conversion neuroses were seen
primarily in women.

picture is dominated by complaints that are referable to the body.

It is convenient to include under the hysterical neuroses the neurosis of secondary gain, or compensation neurosis. In this illness there has usually been some physical pathology in the past, but the symptoms resulting from this organic pathology persist after the organic pathology has been cured. This phenomenon can best be explained by examples. A thirty-five year old mother of three children slips on a banana peel and fractures her spine; she is rushed to a hospital and given orthopedic treatment. Such major organic pathology makes any patient expect pain, inability to move, and other physical symptoms. The results from orthopedic measures are excellent—the orthopedist himself is amazed at the woman's complete recovery; x-rays hardly reveal that anything ever happened to the vertebral column; the family is overjoyed with the results of therapy. Nevertheless, the symptoms of pain and limitation of back motion continue. It then becomes clear to the consulting psychiatrist, although it is not clear to the patient, that she is reacting to the fact that while she was in the hospital her husband hired a maid to cook the meals, do the dishes, make the beds, wipe the children's noses, do the sewing, the laundry, the ironing, etc. When the doctors tell her she is well, it really means to her that she will have to return to an arduous daily routine unless she keeps the pain in her back and, as a secondary gain, the maid in the house. The woman has a neurosis of secondary gain; the symptoms once due to physical pathology persist after it has disappeared and persist for the very purpose of achieving the secondary gain.

These neuroses are often the results of workmen's compensation settlements, automobile accident claim settlements, and settlements made by the United States government to people on active duty in the Armed Forces. For example, a soldier is wounded in line of duty, receives expert treatment, and recovers completely. During the weeks of treatment the soldier had etiologically significant organic pathology to account for his pain and bodily limitations. After the organic pathology is cured, the government tells him, in effect: "You now have a choice. If you get rid of your symptoms of pain and limited motion, we will send you back to active duty and you will have to suffer the hardships of war. On the other hand, if you keep your symptoms, we will discharge you from the Armed Forces and allow you to return to your family and job, and further reward you with a monthly compensation and other benefits. All you have to do is to hold on to your symptoms, because as soon as they stop, we will take all this away from you." The soldier who cannot get rid of his symptoms has a compensation neurosis. This example, of course, is an exception; most veterans receive compensation for bona fide physical pathology.

The above examples of compensation neurosis and neurosis of secondary gain raise the question of malingering, a most serious charge that is hard to prove. The individuals associated with a case of suspected malingering—the patient, the medical doctor, psychiatrist, nurse, the patient's family, the donors of the secondary gain—each have their own opinion which can never be proved right or wrong. In therapy, patients with these neuroses prove most difficult—perhaps because they have so little to gain from recovery.

The hysterical neurosis makes use of the mechanism of conversion and shows, in its clinical picture, only one physical symptom, and thus is called monosymptomatic. The symptom has specific characteristics: it is pseudoneurological in that it displays apparent involvement of either the motor or sensory part of the peripheral nervous system, and it corresponds with the mind's concept of the human body. An hysterical conversion symptom might be a paralyzed right arm, with the forearm, wrist and fingers being perfectly normal. This symptom seems to involve the peripheral nervous system in its motor component, and coincides with the mind's concept that the arm is a functioning unit, notwithstanding the fact that a lesion involving the arm in paralysis would affect the forearm, wrist, and fingers as well. Although such neurotic symptoms cannot be produced by any anatomical lesion, even physicians who are thoroughly versed in anatomy can develop them. Symptoms of conversion hysteria can involve any part of the peripheral nervous system in its motor or sensory component, producing various paralyses and anesthesias, peculiar types of deafness and blindness, bizarre hypermotilities such as tics and spasms, anatomically inexplicable difficulties with walking, talking, etc. There is even a hypermotility of the entire body, quite similar to the convulsions of epilepsy, which is called hystero-epilepsy. It is, however, a conversion neurosis, characterized by the fact that the patient is conscious during the spell, that the spell lasts longer than the usual epileptic convulsion, that the Babinski reflex of the post-epileptic state is not found, and that the spell may consist more of a kind of angry flailing of arms than of a tonic and clonic seizure.

Freud, Breuer,[4] and Charcot[5] did much of their early work with victims of conversion hysteria and discovered

---

[4] Josef Breuer was born in 1842 and died in 1925. He is primarily known for his work in collaboration with Freud during Freud's earlier years. He and Freud jointly authored a book entitled *Studies in Hysteria* which is one of the classics in psychiatric literature. Breuer utilized hypnosis with his neurotic patients, but then introduced the innovation of letting the hypnotized patients talk of what oppressed their minds instead of applying suggestions to them in that state. Thus began the *cathartic* method of treatment which Freud was to refine into the *free association* method.

[5] Jean Martin Charcot was born in 1825 and died in 1893. He laid the foundation for the scientific investigation of mental phenomena. His most original discovery was that a *morbid* or *pathogenic* idea could produce hys-

that the symptom could be removed by hypnosis, even
though it would later return. In the eighteenth century
Mesmer removed conversion symptoms by "the laying on
of hands," which psychiatrists now recognize to have been
largely suggestion. In addition to hypnosis and suggestion,
catharsis, or the process of talking out the problem, was of
some benefit as Freud discovered. When dealing with conversion hysteria, Freud became aware of the patient's characteristic indifference to his symptom—the so-called "belle
indifférence"—and was led to deduce that the symptom must
serve an ulterior purpose. This very deduction led him to
postulate the existence of the unconscious. Modern treatment
of hysterical conversion neuroses is insight therapy, and
prognosis is usually excellent.

The second edition of the *Diagnostic and Statistical
Manual of Mental Disorders* lists nine types of *psychophysiological disorders* or *psychosomatic diseases.* In dealing with
these illnesses, the psychiatrist comes in contact with the
specialists of internal medicine, surgery, dermatology, allergy,
etc., a fact which has produced popular use and acceptance
of the broad concept of psychosomatic medicine. The symptoms of psychosomatic disease have certain common characteristics; they are actual neurological involvements, involving
either the sympathetic or parasympathetic part of the autonomic or vegetative nervous system, and they are bodily
expressions of feelings. Any organ or part of the body sup-
plied by the autonomic or vegetative nervous system can
become host to a psychosomatic disease if it is going to be
used to express an emotion. In psychosomatic illnesses or
psychophysiological diseases, the patient's feelings and

---

terical manifestations, and that both the idea and the symptoms could be
influenced by hypnosis. He linked together the phenomena of hysteria and
hypnotism. Charcot and Freud worked together for a short period of time,
but Freud then carried on these concepts to achieve additional understanding
of mental phenomena.

emotional conflicts are converted or transformed so that they affect his body via the involvement of the autonomic nervous system; in this manner, psychological factors can cause or contribute to the formation of physical disease and pathology. Another category of psychosomatic medicine, called *somato-psychic*, concerns the psychological effects of somatic diseases existing in an individual. Thus, there develops the concept of mind and body as being connected and inter-related, each influencing the other.

Although there are many ways to classify the large number of psychosomatic diseases, psychiatrists prefer to group them in accordance with the stages of libidinal or psychosexual development. In the oral stage are placed psychosomatic diseases like asthma, ulcer, hypersalivation, hyperemesis, etc.; in the anal stage are grouped colitis, either mucous or ulcerative, various diarrheas and constipations, and perhaps even hemorrhoids; in the genital stage are found psychosomatic diseases afflicting the genital apparatus, especially frigidity in the female and impotence in the male. Some psychosomatic diseases, such as hypertension, migraine, and neurodermatitis are difficult to classify according to this schema. Books and articles have been written about all of the many psychosomatic diseases and their etiology or treatment. Nowadays, psychosomatic diseases are best handled by a therapeutic team of doctors, including a psychiatrist as a member of the team; no psychiatrist should have to take full responsibility for a patient with a psychosomatic illness, nor will he wish or be able to do so.

Of greatest benefit to the reader of this book will be a brief discussion of one aspect of psychosomatic diseases, namely, some of the psychophysiological genito-urinary disorders. Material of a scientific nature involving the diseases of frigidity and impotence will be presented and explained. The answer to the moral or religious questions relating to the sexual aspects of life can only be given by the reader himself, according to his beliefs, understanding and philosophy.

In order to understand the illness or abnormality, one must first know normality. The normal sexual act can be divided into three phases, tumescence, orgasm, and detumescence—all three controlled by the autonomic or vegetative nervous system. In the male, tumescence occurs in response to a sexual situation when intercourse is a possibility. The autonomic nervous system causes the veins and capillaries in the penis to dilate and become engorged with blood, making it rigid and erect. Orgasm, caused by frictions applied to the shaft and glans of the penis during the act of intercourse, consists of an ecstatic feeling of relief or release from tension, a rhythmical expansion and contraction of the penis, and the ejaculation of seminal fluid containing spermatozoa. In detumescence, which occurs after the orgasm is completed, the blood drains out of the veins and capillaries of the penis which then resumes its limp state.

In women, too, tumescence occurs in a sexual situation when intercourse is in the offing, but most women need some help in achieving this stage. The husband gives help when he makes love to his wife, caresses her, and pays special attention to her erogenous zones (lips, nipples of the breast, inner aspect of the thighs, clitoris, and the vaginal orifice itself). Her autonomic nervous system is thus stimulated to produce tumescence, characterized mainly by secretion of a lubricating fluid from the glands around the genital opening which are controlled by the autonomic nervous system. Orgasm is caused by frictions applied to the vagina, the labiae, and clitoris by the penis as it is thrust in and out during intercourse. Female orgasm consists of an ecstatic feeling of relief and a release from tension, along with rhythmical dilatations and constrictions of the vagina, labiae and the muscles surrounding the genital tract. Whether or not ejaculation of fluid is part of the female orgasm is a debatable point; if there is an ejaculation, it consists of fluid from the glands which supply the lubricating fluid or from the glands in the cervix. Detumescence occurs after the orgasm is completed and is characterized by return of the woman's psychological and physiological state to its usual quiescence.

Statistics on the act of sexual intercourse emphasize the wide range of normality. The normal frequency of inter-course—not including here young honeymooners or elderly couples—ranges from once every other week to once a night. Within this normal range, the average frequency, or that with which most married couples have intercourse, is about two or three times a week. A frequency of less than every other week or more than every night is considered beyond the limits of normality and is thus abnormal. Duration of intercourse, defined by the amount of friction necessary to produce a climax or orgasm and excluding time spent in fore- or after-play, again is very variable, extending from a minimum of three minutes to a maximum of fifteen. If the movements causing friction consume less than three or more than fifteen minutes, the time is considered beyond the limits of normal and the intercourse is thus abnormal. The average duration of friction in intercourse is about five to seven minutes.

With this knowledge of the normal as a reference, it is possible to consider the abnormal—the inability for satis-factory, enjoyable intercourse, called frigidity in women and impotence in men. These psychosomatic diseases must be sharply differentiated from sterility and infertility which have to do with ovarian functioning, patency of the uterine tubes, quantity and quality of sperm, in short, with problems associated with pregnancy, whereas frigidity and impotence do not usually cause childlessness in marriage.

There are various forms of *impotence,* or inability for satisfactory, enjoyable intercourse in men. Some men have trouble with tumescence; some can have an erection only with another man, and find it impossible with a woman; others are incapable of achieving erection with either men or women; while still others require some particular situations and conditions in order to achieve erection. Another category of impotence consists of difficulty with orgasm; men so afflicted either reach orgasm too soon in so-called *premature ejaculation,* or too late in so-called *retarded ejaculation.* The severest degree of premature ejaculation occurs in men who have erections without difficulty but then ejaculate before they are able to insert their penis into the vagina. This type of impotence, called *ejaculatio ante portas,* can and does result in childless marriages since the sperm is not deposited in the vagina whence it can find its way to the ovum or egg of the female.

Frigidity, or inability for satisfactory, enjoyable intercourse in women, also occurs in a variety of ways. Some women have trouble achieving tumescence, so that it is impossible or difficult for them to secrete sufficient lubrication to allow intercourse to progress, resulting in the symptom of dyspareunia, or painful intercourse. Like a cough, dyspareunia can have many different causes, but in addition to such physical causes as tuberculosis of the female genital tract, the possibility of a psychological basis must be kept in mind. Many women with difficulty in lubrication not only have unresponsive vaginas—so-called vaginal anesthesia—but also are unresponsive emotionally. Another category of frigidity is seen in women who lubricate adequately but then have difficulty in achieving a climax or orgasm. Although they can become pregnant, intercourse for them is not emotionally rewarding or gratifying; instead of finding ecstasy and fulfillment in intercourse, they are left tense, unrelieved and frustrated. Some women with this condition indulge in "hysterics" by writhing about in bed, flailing their husbands with their fists or biting them with their teeth, having what is essentially a temper tantrum; many more blame their husbands instead of facing difficulties which exist within themselves. The causes of the psychosomatic diseases of frigidity and impotence are almost always psychological. Characteristically, the impotent man would himself prefer to be a woman and has unconsciously identified with his mother instead of his father; in his marriage, he does not want to take on the responsibilities of a husband, and lets his wife run the show; in his relationship to her, he unconsciously both fears and hates her, and uses his symptom of impotence as a way of expressing these feelings. The typical frigid woman would prefer to be a man since, in solving her Oedipus complex, she has identified with her father instead of her mother; in her marriage she is aggressive and domineering, inclined to badger and belittle her husband; in her sexual relationship with him she usually both hates and fears him in her unconscious mind and uses her symptom of frigidity as a way of expressing these feelings.

The therapy of frigidity and impotence is insight psychotherapy or psychoanalysis, and the results are nearly always excellent. The use of hormonal or endocrinological preparations, of prostatic massage, urethral instillations, and operative procedures such as suspension of the uterus, all are of no avail; such procedures, however, are all too frequently employed, accomplishing little more than fixation of symptoms and increased difficulty for the psychiatrist.

These psychophysiological genito-urinary disorders not only illustrate the general nature of psychosomatic illnesses very well and have great theoretical interest, but are also of practical significance, for the sexual aspects of marriage are certainly important. Sexual incompatibility is a newspaper term for the psychophysiological genito-urinary disorders of

frigidity and impotence, and one has only to scan the average
newspaper to see how often it is mentioned as the reason for
divorce. Psychiatrists would like to substitute for divorce
an attempt to help people involved in marital and sexual
maladjustment to a happier, more satisfying life by understanding them and by helping them to understand
themselves.

This concludes the survey of psychiatric diseases. Figure
8 summarizes the diseases in terms of the anatomy of the
personality, while Table 3 summarizes the diseases in terms
of psychosexual or libidinal development.

RECOMMENDED READING

*For complete bibliographic data, see also the General Bibliography
following the Preface.*

Abraham: *Selected Papers,* pp. 64-79, 280-298, and 338-369.

Batchelor: *Henderson and Gillespie's Textbook of Psychiatry,* chapter 8.

English and Pearson: *Common Neuroses of Children and Adults,* pp.
189-293.

Ewalt and Farnsworth: *Textbook of Psychiatry,* chapters 8 and 9.

Fenichel: *The Psychoanalytic Theory of Neurosis,* chapters 7-15.

Hendrick: *Facts and Theories of Psychoanalysis,* chapters 9, 10.

Hitschmann, E., and Bergler, E. *Frigidity in Women.* Baltimore:
Williams and Wilkins, 1948.

Kolb: *Noyes' Modern Clinical Psychiatry,* chapters 27 and 28.

Mezer, R. R. "Psychiatric Aspects of Ulcerative Colitis." *American Journal of Proctology,* 1955, *6*:387-390.

Weiss, E., and English, O. S. *Psychosomatic Medicine.* Philadelphia:
W. B. Saunders, 1957.

Table 3 TOTAL SUMMARY

	Pre-oral (non-verbal)	Oral	Anal	Genital
Social Behavior	Pleasure	Pleasure (love)	Compliance with external authority	Compliance with internal, self-contained moral code
Character Traits	Omnipotent, megalomanic, narcissistic	Passive, dependent (oral activity)	Hostile, sadistic (clean, neat, punctual, stingy, meticulous, pedantic)	Aggressive, independent (genital activity)
Characteristic Ego Defenses	Denial, withdrawal, regression, projection	Introjection, incorporation	Extrojection	Identification, sublimation, repression
Psychosis	Schizophrenia	Manic-Depressive; Involutional Melancholia	—	—
Neurosis	—	Neurotic affective disorders (reactive depression and delayed grief reaction)	Obsessive-compulsive neurosis; neurasthenia	Anxiety neurosis; phobic neurosis; hysterical conversion neurosis
Psychophysiological Disorders *	Neurodermatitis; arthritis	Ulcer; asthma; migraine	Ulcerative colitis; hypertension	Frigidity; impotence

*This is the author's personal concept; many would argue and disagree with this organization of psychosomatic diseases.

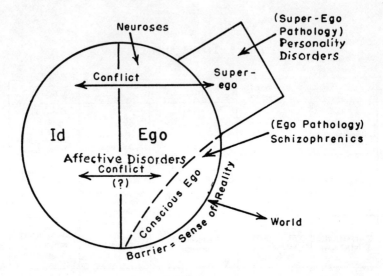

Fig. 8   Total summary of psychiatric diseases and pathology of personality.

In schizophrenics, the ego is involved—ego breakdown, a malignancy of the ego. In affectives, there may be a conflict between hostility from the id and the ego; the ego, unable to handle the hostility in a mature, socially acceptable form (sublimation), has to introject it (depression) or extroject it (manic states). In personality disorders, the super-ego is disturbed in its relationship to the ego which tends to act out conflicts. In neurotics, the ego is faced with a conflict between the desire to express an id impulse and the inhibition against expressing it (super-ego and society).

PART IV

Outlook

CHAPTER 12

The Normal Life

This book began by describing the development of the normal personality; the various illnesses of a psychiatric nature were then considered; an over-all view of the normal life closes the ring—showing that most people pass through the danger zones of life not much the worse for the experience, and continue steadily in their pursuit of happiness.

Life begins with birth. In the vast majority of cases, delivery and birth are uncomplicated, ending with a healthy baby and a healthy mother. Once born, the baby must begin to live life. Quite helpless and incapable in the early days, he depends almost entirely on his environment for his sustenance and his very existence. As he begins to mature physically and becomes more capable of caring for himself, he develops an ever-increasing independence, self-sufficiency, or autonomy. As the child becomes ready to do things for himself, normal parents let him take over and even encourage him to do so, but at the same time they stand by to assist him if his capacities should prove insufficient for the new task. It is difficult to say how early in life independence begins to develop; it may occur in bowel training, walking, weaning—perhaps even when the number of feedings is reduced for the first time. Regardless of the particular moment, the factors of the child's increasing capacities and the parent's allowing them to develop are always present, so that there can exist a harmony and balance between these two forces. The understanding parent does not set the pace for the child's growth and maturing but waits for their emergence and then approves the use of the newly found power, while standing ready to lend support if failure seems imminent. Such an attitude on the part of the parents is important to the child's development. Psychiatrists know only too well the results of the demanding attitude of parents. They see the people who fulfill their parents' expectations to a "T" but are miserably unhappy because they are not true to themselves. These people feel as if they had a facade, a false front; nothing they do, no matter how well, gives them pleasure or reward, for they are merely doing what their parents expect. Parents who inflict themselves, their hopes, wants, demands and expectations, on their children are selfish people, driven by their own frustrations. Fortunately, most parents allow their children to mature as nature intended.

It is normal for children to want and need love, and it is normal for parents to love their children. But how does one define this love? Many parents who are baffled at how their children turn out cannot comprehend how such an unhappy product could result from their rearing. Their universal statement is: "I can't understand it, I loved my child, I gave my child everything." Then follows a list of material things such as clothes, food, money, schooling, replete with examples of parental self-sacrifice. True, man now lives in a world which is becoming more and more materialistic, but materialistic giving and self-sacrifice do not equal love. Normal love is a free-flowing feeling that comes from understanding, approval, and acceptance. This is what the growing child needs and deserves. Love is to him an atmosphere in which he is accepted as he is, was, and will be.

Interpersonal relationships begin at birth, the first person-to-person contact being that of the child with his parents. This relationship is basic. It is the precursor of all other relationships which are to follow with siblings, playmates, classmates, colleagues, teachers, bosses, husbands and wives, and offspring. One grows and matures in proportion to one's feeling secure. Security means self-satisfaction and self-acceptance. Security develops if the child gets the love, just defined above, in his first interpersonal relationship. Only then can the child feel strong enough to try the next step in his growth, namely, to venture upon interpersonal relationships outside of his immediate family. When he feels secure with his parents, he can be so with other children and, later on, have friendships; he need not spend a secluded, isolated, or solitary existence. People who complain of loneliness, who can feel alone and isolated even in a group, may suffer this handicap because they felt rejected and unwanted by their parents.

Since in most families there is more than one child, it is necessary to consider the problem of siblings—a problem that exists only if the parents make it so. It is probably inevitable that the first born feels replaced by the second, that the oldest is envied his privileges while the youngest is envied because he is "the baby," that those in the middle feel neglected because they have no special identity, and so on. Thus begin sibling rivalry and jealousy, unless parents get across to their children that each is loved equally although in a different way. Johnny should know that he is loved because he is a boy, and Jane because she is a girl;

that the oldest is loved because he is the biggest, the youngest because he is the smallest, but all of them to the same
degree. It is an inexpressible relief to the child to feel that
he is loved and accepted, to know that he belongs.

Children want to express themselves freely, but it is un-
fair to let a child grow up with the idea that all is permitted,
nothing forbidden, that he can "get what he wants when
he wants it." Life is not set up this way, and most children
feel relieved when parents establish a realistic limit within
which they can operate and express themselves. To do this
without making the child feel criticized and "no good,"
parents may instill in him the idea and feeling that while
he himself is loved, and his feelings, impulses and desires are
understood and accepted, there is nevertheless a real difference between *wanting* to do things and actually *doing* them.
He can be brought to understand that it is the actual doing,
his *behavior,* which is disapproved of, but that he himself
is still loved, understood and accepted. Even a child would
understand why a policeman directing traffic holds up his
hand: he stops a car from crossing an intersection, but does
not condemn the driver for wanting to get across or for
being a motorist. This is an example of a realistic limit set
by an authority figure. Furthermore, once the limit is set,
it stays; despite impatience, rebellion, hostility, and furor,
the stop signal stands firm. Can one imagine a policeman
letting the horn-tooting lane of traffic go first? Yet, this is in
essence what parents often do. They set a limit which is
realistic, but when the child rebels and gets angry they say,
"Well, okay, but just this once." In so doing, they negate
and weaken the very limits they have set. This also proves
upsetting to the child who no longer has any frame of reference that is realistic and reliable and within which he can
operate. If "no" doesn't mean "no," then what does anything

mean? When parents speak of a spoiled child, they are really saying, "Here's the product of our inconsistent rearing pattern."

From time immemorial the problem of discipline has plagued parents, while the pendulum has swung from the doctrine of "children should be seen and not heard" to that of free expression. At present the trend is verging on a child tyranny in which Junior governs the mealtime hours and conversation, dictates the television programs, receives every toy he desires, and, in general, rules the roost. "No!" has been struck out of parental vocabularies. In the main, this philosophy of free expression has resulted from misinterpretation of psychological writings. Lacking perspective, parents simply decide not to do what has been condemned and go to the opposite extreme. There is no easy road to successful child discipline. An "all black or all white" attitude, while underestimating the dangers and pitfalls of the extremes, neglects the normal realistic "middle road." To give parents specific instructions on how to handle each and every disciplinary problem not only would be a hopeless task but also would belittle the intelligence of the average couple and deprive them of the joy of finding their own solutions. Taking the middle road requires common sense and moderation.

Education is a normal experience in every life. Some people go so far as to say that living is merely a process of learning. How important, then, are the school years, especially those spent in nursery school, kindergarten and first grade. Teachers nowadays are growing ever more aware of their responsibility of having to go beyond the teaching of "the three R's;" they know that they must instill in the child a zest for future learning. In any child a feeling of accomplishment and a sense of reward in his studies are

prerequisites for the development of the avid desire to learn.
Many problems in reading and speaking (especially stam-
mering and difficulty in speaking in public) and many learning blocks (frequently seen in the areas of arithmetic and
spelling) begin because of unwise attitudes in teachers and
parents during the early years of schooling. Each child, it
must be remembered, develops at his own pace. After an era
that demanded of any child conformity with others of his
chronological age, parents and teachers of today are aware
that each child has his own capacities, assets and liabilities,
all of which are in a tremendous and wonderful state of
flux. What can ever be gained by criticizing, condemning,
and punishing a child for inabilities beyond his control and
just as bothersome to him as to his teachers and parents?
Pernicious, too, is the old punishment of ostracism from a
group to which the child wants and needs to belong, of
making him "sit in the corner;" or the humiliating policy
of criticizing him and berating him in front of the other
children. Parents and teachers learn as they live life, just as
do children. Mistakes are inevitable, and in correcting them
lies growth and progress. "Knowing all the answers" is mere
smugness, for what is in vogue and correct today will be
forgotten or condemned tomorrow.

Although raising children is not at all an easy task,
parents are generally aware that worthwhile things come
only from combining much effort and exertion with some
worry and apprehension. The job of parents is to provide a
loving atmosphere and to set realistic limits for their children; the job of children is to grow up in this atmosphere,
and learn and mature within these realistic limits. The result is usually a happy adolescent, and —what is not to be
omitted—happy parents!

Adolescence is always spoken of as something very new
and difficult, but this is not exactly the case. Adolescence is

not difficult in the sense of being different from what has
gone before; rather, it is difficult because it is a repetition
of what has gone before, and because the repetition is of
greater intensity. In adolescence there occurs an upsurge of
energy which is both physical and psychological. Many adolescents, both boys and girls, go through a complete Oedipus
complex again at this stage in their lives, with the difference
that now the entire gamut of positive and negative feelings
is expressed more verbally and intensely, although not necessarily more directly. The boy and his father threaten to
come to blows; the girl and her mother are in open opposition, rebellion and hostility. The father finds his son in-
corrigible, while the mother finds her daughter unmanage-
able. Adolescence is a period requiring the utmost in love,
acceptance and understanding on the part of parents who, at
the same time—for the sake of self-preservation—must set
realistic and consistently maintained limits.

It has often been observed that the adolescent shows
marked inconsistencies and contradictions, and that one finds
babyhood and adulthood coexisting or alternating within
him. Yet, coexistence of the old, which has been tried and
proved, with the new, which has still to be tried and proved,
was characteristic of all preceding growth processes. As a
baby starts to walk, he tries out the new by taking his first
step and then promptly reverts to the proved old way of
crawling or sitting down. This same process of alternately
trying out the new (independence or growing up in a social
sense) and falling back on the old (dependency) is typical of
adolescence, the only difference being one of intensity. An
adolescent cannot simply jump into adulthood any more
than a crawling baby can run a race; there has to be a process of trial, of gaining acceptance and approval, of feeling
secure and then progressing further until what was new becomes familiar and old. Once this pattern is understood, **it**

seems strange that some parents criticize adolescents for being babies, while they would never dream of criticizing a baby for sitting down while learning to walk.

Since social life is a most important area in the experience and learning of adolescence, one sees very early in this period the emergence of groups. These groups or clubs, usually composed of members of the same sex, are of the utmost importance, because they are the precursors of adult participation in social groups and clubs, of belonging to a political party or religious group. They are the links between belonging in one's family and belonging in the world of others, society. The adolescent groups perform another vital function in that they provide for their members the acceptance and understanding which all too often cannot be found in the home or anywhere else outside these groups. They accept the adolescent as a "baby," encourage him as he becomes ready to try out "adulthood," and stand behind him in case the going becomes too difficult.

In later adolescence, dating of the opposite sex begins; here again, the process starts off with group dates but with both sexes now intermingling. The group affords support and encouragement as experience in adult living is being learned. After the adolescent feels secure in his group and gang get-togethers, he will try double-dating, and finally, when he is ready, he solos. Much furor exists over this phenomenon of dating, which is nothing but another learning experience in life. As boys and girls go together and date each other, they learn not only about themselves but also about others. Such evaluation of self and of others, such sifting of the important from the unimportant, such sorting out of the meaningful qualities in other persons is a normal, necessary and vital process by which the adolescent arrives at an ideal, the type of person he would like to marry.

Formation of an ideal or idol is not the end of the road; the normal adolescent gradually comes face to face with reality and sees that his ideal type of mate is phantasied but not available. Then comes the process of settling or compromise, of accepting the individual who is realistically available. The process repeats the solution of the Oedipus complex—the testing of reality and accepting of realistic limits, which is so basic to the normal development that it is repeated over and over throughout life. The individual who has had the maturity to accept reality, though cloaking it with the adoring feelings of love and reverence once felt toward the ideal, is now ready for marriage.

No marriage exists merely because a legal paper certifies that it is one; marriages must be worked on, if they are to continue. Whenever one sees a happily married couple, one can be certain that they worked hard to achieve their happiness and harmony. One important aspect of working on a marriage is the capacity to stop and take a look, the ability to submerge for the moment one's own desires and demands, to see how realistic they are and whether or not they are capable of fulfillment, and then either to accept the situation as it is or try to change it. Psychiatrists listen to husbands and wives who, usually, did not stop and take a look—each mate complaining about the other, each wanting the other to change, to fulfill an ideal. Wives wish their husbands were "more romantic," "more affectionate," "not only interested in sex;" husbands wish their wives were "more interested in sex," "not so demanding or domineering," "more interested in me than in the family." To demand or expect the perfect mate is normal in adolescence, but it is immature and neurotic in adulthood.

Another way of working on a marriage is to keep the channels of communication open. Normal and inevitable

differences and disagreements in marriage must be commu-
nicated. The partners must listen as well as talk. Unless
channels of communication remain open both ways, there
can only be bickering, arguing, claims that "I'm right and
you're wrong" and the accompanying dangerous feeling of
omnipotent self-righteousness. Although the world of today
is wonderfully complex, there are people who manage to
feel wholly sure that they are always right, that they know
all the angles to any difficult problem. Psychiatrists are in a
good position to know such people. It must be admitted,
however, that there are even psychiatrists who are so omnipotent, so cocksure, so defensively self-righteous, that they
think they know all the answers. Such psychiatrists are to
be avoided, not so much because they may be wrong (who
is to judge, or who can judge?), but rather because they are
unable to listen.

Since the parents of the husband and the wife, the in-
laws, are added to most marriages, the difficulties in adjustment increase. Soap-operas, television plays, and newspaper
cartoons to the contrary, there need not be a continued in-
law problem. Although no one solution is universally ap-
plicable, the rule that each shall handle his own frequently
proves helpful; the husband handles his parents, while
the wife handles hers, on the assumption that, since blood
is thicker than water, parents will accept from a son or
daughter what they would never accept from a son-in-law or
daughter-in-law. Thus, the latter can stay clear of disputes
with the partner's parents and remain the perfect, sweet,
kind, wonderful, considerate, thoughtful son-in-law or
daughter-in-law. Whenever a parent is heard to state, "My
daughter-in-law is better than my own son," evidence is
being given of the practical use of the above rule. There
is only one hitch, namely, the question of whether a person

has the capacity to handle his or her own parents. In deciding on a marital partner, one should seriously evaluate the capacities of the prospective partner to handle his or her parents, to "stop and take a look" and "to keep the channels of communication open." Psychiatrists, in finding out why people got married, why they chose each other, constantly hear such give-away statements as, "She was so like my mother," "We enjoyed arguing with each other," "I felt I'd lose her if I didn't, but I wasn't sure," "It was a challenge to see if I could get him to be affectionate," "My mother convinced and persuaded me," "He danced divinely," "She had money and could support me," "He was so helpless, I pitied him," and so on, *ad nauseam*. Much attention is now being given to divorce which is an important problem, if not always a tragedy; at the same time one must remember that most marriages are happy and enduring institutions.

No discussion of marriage is complete without reference to the "roles" of marital partners. In families, there are two main patterns of stratification, matriarchy and patriarchy. In a matriarchy the wife or mother is boss, while in a patriarchy the husband or father rules. Children, growing up, witness the dominance of either mother or father. It will be recalled that the normal Oedipus complex results in identification with the parent of the same sex. If a boy grows up in a patriarchal family, thus identifying with his dominant father, while a girl grows up in a matriarchal family, identifying with her dominant mother, imagine what would happen if this boy and girl should marry. Each would feel entitled to be boss and each could look back to the parent of the same sex as proof. The result would be friction and disharmony. Psychiatry favors a patriarchy as being more normal; most psychiatrists, however, are men so that their position could be a defense or an attempt at self-preservation.

More important than the problem of whether patriarchy or matriarchy is the more normal and healthy—since perfect equality is impossible, every family has to be one or the other—is the question of the ability of the marital partners to get along with each other in harmonious agreement. Fortunately, the children of matriarchies are usually attracted to each other, as are the children of patriarchies, so that the normal marriage avoids a conflict of roles.

Much has already been said about the problem of raising children into healthy and happy adults. Mothers and fathers are frequently bothered by the specific problem of giving their children a proper sex education. Parents nowadays feel it proper and decent and, indeed, necessary to give children "the facts of life;" they raise the question of *how* to go about it. Again, there is no one right way that makes all others wrong; certain guiding principles, however, can be very helpful to parents. One principle is to be truthful. Imagine a child who grows up believing he was brought by a stork. What feelings will he have toward his parents when he discovers that they deceived him? What feelings will he have toward sex? What will his sexual adjustment in marriage be like? If it is all right to know that two and two make four, or that Christopher Columbus discovered America in 1492, why then, the child reasons, is it not all right to know the facts of life? Next comes the question of *how much* of the truth parents should tell. A child four or five years old—and questions about sexual matters do begin even before these ages—certainly cannot understand the facts about spermatozoa, ova, or intercourse. He wants and needs a truthful answer to his question, but an answer that is on his own level, as much as he is ready for, and something he can understand and accept. When the four or five-year old asks, "Where do babies come from?" a truthful and comprehensible answer might be, "From a special part of mommy's body." Given naturally and without embarrassment, the answer will satisfy the child's question and, at the same time, leave the way open for further elaborations and details in the future. But too often the child's early inquiries are met with such disapproving remarks from the parent as, "Ask your father," "I'm busy now, don't bother me," "Wait until you're older," "That's not a nice question to ask," "Nice people don't talk of such things." The child clams up, refusing to confide in his parents, feeling that to ask about such things is forbidden.

If early questions are answered naturally, truthfully, concisely and understandably, further questions will follow. When the child has assimilated the previous answers and is ready to seek for more information, the whole wonderful story of procreation can little by little be imparted, creating a bond between parent and child and a tremendous feeling of security for the child who feels *he* knows what his parents know.

Parents often want to know *who* should give the information and *when* it should be given. In general, the person asked the question is the natural one to answer it then and there. If one parent is biased or unrealistic, or feels embarrassed when discussing sexual matters, then by all means the other parent ought to do the job. All too frequently, the job is shunted onto the family doctor. Factual information, however, is only part of the requirement, the other being the attitude or the way in which the information is given. Ideally and normally, no book, no talk by a stranger, no course in school can take the place of sexual education by the parents in the home.

A big segment of normal life usually consists of work. Regardless of the type or level of a job, work can give an important feeling of usefulness to life and contribute a lot to the individual's "joie de vivre." Work can also be a bore, a duty, or a chore, depending on the individual's attitude which, like most adult attitudes, has its origin in early life. One can say that in childhood work is play, or that the play of childhood is work. Children enjoy playing, being industrious, getting the feeling of accomplishment. They keep running to their parents to exclaim, "Look, mommy, look what I made!" and expect in return praise and encouragement. It is ironical that the very parents who are too busy to compliment the early undertakings of their children, who do not take the time to be with, play with, and work with their children, are the parents who later expect their adult sons and daughters to be productive and industrious. It's too late then, for the parents have long squelched all joy in working and playing in their children. Robbed of an important area of gratification and reward in life, the offspring is in a spot even more lamentable than that of his parents. Fortunately, the average child gets enough gratification from play and from approval of such activity to feel secure enough to learn in school, and secure enough to work and labor in adulthood—not only secure enough but actually able to enjoy a job.

Interpersonal relationships on the job are an important part of living. The problem may be that of getting an employee's cooperation, of keeping a worker interested in the job, of dealing with absenteeism, etc. or of determining desirable characteristics in the boss—how demanding, how critical, how understanding, how sympathetic he should be. Even in today's complex industrial organizations, certain basic principles of relations within the family apply: namely, understanding, acceptance, and approval coming from both management and labor, as well as realistic limits which are consistently maintained. Although labor disputes and strikes receive much attention, they remain exceptions; most working "families" or organizations are healthy and happy units just as most private families are.

Like most things in nature, people start off with a small beginning, grow and mature, reach a peak, and then begin a decline. Appropriately enough, this period of change from increase to decrease is called "the change of life." The chronological age at which this change occurs not only varies with the individual but also seems to be occurring at an increasingly later age as the general life span increases. The change of life is characterized in women by a cessation of menstruation and sometimes in men by a decrease in sexual desire or capacity; in addition, both men and women experience a psychological or emotional change of life, marked by self-reflection and self-evaluation and a realization that the time of decline is ahead.

The problems of the change of life seldom begin at this stage of life. What usually happens is that problems which have been lying dormant for years become exposed and cause difficulties by demanding solutions. A frequent and pitiful example is the problem of the woman who has lived a life of self-sacrifice for her children, who has totally subjugated herself to her family. To lose the physiological ability to have children is an overwhelming blow to her, because one of the most important parts of her existence has been to have children. When her children grow up, marry, and leave her "alone," the loss is completed. Frequently, such a woman never had a good relationship with her husband; it sometimes seems as if she had used the husband for stud purposes only and relegated him, along with everything else that life offers, to a position secondary to her children. Such a woman, at change of life, will find herself in a tough spot.

People are apt to forget that they have strengths and

capacities within themselves upon which they can rely, that they have the ability to shape their own destinies and to plan their own futures. Life is not a one-way street; the normal life reaches out into many different directions simultaneously. It is concerned with children, family, friends, marriage, work, hobbies, recreations, social activities, physical activities, religion, intellectual and artistic pursuits—the more the merrier, the greater the diversity the healthier, the greater the intensity the happier!

When one has lived a well-rounded life, there need not be special problems during the change of life or during old age. One has learned to adjust, to adapt, to compromise and to sublimate, to be realistic about one's self and about others. This is the true wisdom of the advanced years. It is not intellectual but experiential; it comes from living life, experiencing and experimenting and gaining in self-confidence and self-knowledge. One of the frequent events in modern society is enforced retirement at a set chronological age. Maybe such relegation of some very capable and useful human beings is a social necessity; it need not be a tragedy for those affected if they can plan for themselves. For the vast majority, retirement is not synonymous with inactivity; it seldom means that the individual himself is psychologically or physically ready for inactivity. Few retired people nowadays feel discarded to uselessness but continue to live interesting, vital, and useful lives, albeit perhaps in different areas.

The person who has lived through a normal life can look backward with satisfaction and a true sense of fulfillment. When, finally, death arrives, he is ready. To him dying may be the last necessary great experience of living.

Glossary

Affect—feeling.

Aggression—activity or feeling based on anger.

Alcoholism—state of excessive indulgence in alcohol.

Ambivalence—simultaneous presence of two opposing feelings, for example, love and hate.

Ambiversion—the fairly equal mixture of *extroversion* and *introversion,* which see.

Anal eroticism—a term used in psychoanalytic theory to describe the concentration of feelings and interest on the anal region as a pregenital phase of psychosexual development.

Anxiety—apprehension and dread without apparent cause; fear.

Asthenic—in Kretschmer's terminology, descriptive of the type of human physique with small trunk and long limbs, frequently associated with schizophrenia.

Autism—phantasy world created by the patient which is of special significance to him.

Babinski reflex—extension, instead of flexion, of the toes when the sole of the foot is stimulated. Normal in infancy, but a sign of cerebrospinal disorder in later life.

Castration anxiety—anxiety and fear associated with the idea of harm to, or removal of, the sex glands or organs in both men and women.

Castration complex—a complex caused by castration anxiety.

Catatonic—descriptive of a form of schizophrenia in which the patient is either overactive or underactive.

Catharsis—a term used in psychiatry to describe the freeing of repressed feelings.

Cerea flexibilitas—a symptom of catatonic schizophrenia in which the patient retains the position in which his body and limbs have been placed.

Clitoral stage—the period when sexual interest becomes focused on the clitoris during psychosexual development in the female. Comparable to the phallic stage.

Collective unconscious—a term used by Jung to describe the theory that the individual's unconscious is a collection of those elements derived from the experiences of his race.

163

Compensation—an unconscious mechanism by which the patient denies a weakness or defect by exaggerating a lesser or more desirable characteristic.

Complex—a compilation of emotional feelings.

Compulsion—an inner force which compels the patient to act against his own conscious will.

Conflict—opposition between contradictory forces.

Confusion—a mental symptom involving a clouding of consciousness and a lack of orientation.

Congenital—inherited; actually or potentially present at birth.

Conscience—a system of moral principles.

Constitution—the individual's present physical and mental condition and his future development as determined by the detailing of hereditary factors.

Conversion—the transformation of repressed complexes into physical symptoms.

Cunnilingus—a sexual perversion involving the oral stimulation of the female genitals.

Cyclothymic—alternating in moods of happiness and sadness.

Defective delinquent—a delinquent who is mentally deficient.

Defense mechanism—an unconscious device adopted as a means of protection against the painful *affect* associated with distressing physical or mental situations.

Delinquent—a term usually applied to a young offender and to lesser offences than the term *criminal* describes.

Delusion—a false belief.

Dementia—a condition characterized by loss of mental ability.

Dementia praecox—now known as *schizophrenia,* which see.

Depersonalization—a condition in which the patient experiences a sense of unreality to the extent that he may feel that he is someone else or that he no longer exists.

Depression—an emotional attitude or illness involving feelings of sadness and helplessness.

Disassociation—functional interruption of associations or connections in the mind upon which the recall of memories and the systematization of ideas depend.

Disorientation—the individual's loss of his perception of his relationship to time and place.

Displacement—the transfer of affect from one object or person to another to which it does not belong, as in phobias.

Dysarthria—difficulty in articulation of speech; present in some patients with cerebral lesions or disease.

Dyspareunia—painful sexual intercourse.

Ego—awareness of one's self.

Elation—an emotional state characterized by intense excitement.

Emission—see *Nocturnal emissions.*

Emotion—a psychological feeling.

Empathy—a "feeling into" or "feeling for."

Epilepsy—a disorder of the nervous system characterized by seizures or fits occurring at irregular intervals.

Euphoria—intense feeling of well-being.

Exhibitionism—a sexual perversion in which one receives stimulation or satisfaction from exposing one's self.

Extroversion—characterizes the type of personality whose interests are directed outward.

Fellatio—a sexual perversion in which the penis is placed in the mouth of the sexual partner.

Flexibilitas, cerea—see *Cerea flexibilitas.*

Frigidity—a term used to describe in women the absence of normal sexual desire or the inability to be satisfied by normal sexual intercourse.

Furor—an acute emotional state accompanied by violent behavior.

Genital stage—in men and women, a stage of psychosexual development during which feelings and interests are centered on the genital area.

Group psychotherapy—psychotherapeutic treatment undertaken with several individual patients at once.

Guilt—sense of wrong-doing.

Hallucination—a false sensory perception.

Hate—a feeling in which anger predominates.

Hebephrenic—a form of schizophrenia in which the patient is childish and exhibits silly mannerisms.

Heterosexual—sexually attracted toward a member of the opposite sex.

Homosexual—sexually attracted toward a member of the same sex. See *Inversion.*

Hypnosis—the artificial induction of a trance-like state, similar to sleep but characterized by increased suggestibility.

Hypochondria—the excessive anxiety and concern for one's state of health.

Hypomania—state of overexcitability.

Hysteria—condition occuring as a result of the use of the unconscious defense mechanism of *conversion* by the ego. Emotional conflicts are transformed so that they exert a physical influence upon the body.

Ideas of reference—the referral to the self of events and things in the outside world.

Identification—the process of incorporating into one's self the traits and characteristics of another person.

Impotence—in men, the inability to perform intercourse in a satisfactory and enjoyable manner. See *Premature ejaculation; Retarded ejaculation.*

Inadequate personality—one who is unable to cope with the demands of life.

Inferiority complex—in Adlerian psychology, the term refers to a basic psychological or organic weakness.

Insanity—a medico-legal term which is used in situations involving legal irresponsibility and incompetency.

Insight—awareness of one's mental condition.

Insomnia—inability to sleep.

Instincts—primary, congenital motive forces within the individual.

Intelligence—the ability to reason.

Introjection—turning inward onto, or into, the self, for example, anger, the image of another person, etc.

Introversion—characterizes the type of personality whose interests are directed inward.

Intuition—sense of perception and judgment arrived at through the emotions rather than through reason.

Inversion—reversal of the sexual object so that the sexual object becomes a member of the same sex. See *Homosexuality.*

Involutional melancholia—see *Melancholia, involutional.*

Involutional psychosis—a mental illness occurring in mid-life.

Juvenile delinquent—see *Delinquent.*

Korsakoff's psychosis—a mental disorder, usually of alcoholic origin, characterized by weakness of memory, disorientation, a liking for the "tall story" and the symptoms of peripheral polyneuritis.

Latency period—term used to describe the period of psychosexual development extending approximately from the sixth year to the thirteenth year of life.

Lesbian—a female homosexual.

Libido—psychosexual energy and drive.

Lobotomy—a neurosurgical operation involving the prefrontal area of the brain.

Love—range of positive emotions.

Mania—extreme excitement.

Manic-depressive psychosis—a mental disorder involving periods of excitement and depression.

Masochism—sexual satisfaction or pleasure received from suffering pain.

Masturbation—manipulation of the sexual organs to produce pleasure and satisfaction.

Melancholia, involutional—depression occurring in mid-life, characterized by the combination of agitation and depression.

Mental deficiency—insufficient ability to reason.

Mood—feeling or affect.

Narcosynthesis—inducement of a hypnotic trance by the use of Pentothal® (thiopental) or Sodium Amytal® (amobarbital).

Neologism—a word invented by the patient with wholly personal meaning and significance.

Neurosis—see *Psychoneurosis*.

Nocturnal emissions—ejaculations occurring at night, associated with pleasant dreams of a sexual nature.

Obsession—persistent, recurrent thought or idea which forces itself into the mind of an individual against his will.

Oedipus complex—an important phase of psychosexual development evolving between the ages of four and six when the child has positive feelings toward the parent of the opposite sex and negative feelings toward the parent of the same sex. The term is derived from the Greek legend dramatized by Sophocles, in which Oedipus unknowingly kills his father and marries his mother.

Oral character neurosis—neurosis cause by early maladjustment at the oral stage of psychosexual development, characterized by passivity and overdependency.

Oral stage—psychosexual stage of development in which interest and feelings are focused on eating and other oral activities.

Organic psychosis—see *Organic reaction type*.

Organic reaction type—a category of mental conditions in which the brain is organically disturbed by tumor, infection, trauma, senility, etc., and characterized by deterioration of orientation, memory, intelligence, and judgment.

Orgasm—sexual climax.

Orientation—awareness of time, place, and circumstances.

Paranoid—descriptive of a form of mental illness in which there is a delusional system usually persecutory in nature.

Personality—the sum of an individual's reactions to circumstances.

Perversions—deviations in the aim of the sexual instinct.

Phallic stage—period of psychosexual development, usually beginning around the thirteenth year of life, when the boy's sexual interest becomes focused on the penis. Comparable to the clitoral stage in girls.

Phobia—uncontrollable fear of usually one object or situation.

Prefrontal lobotomy—see *Lobotomy*.

Premature ejaculation—condition in which the man reaches orgasm too soon for satisfactory, enjoyable intercourse. See *Impotence*.

Projection—unconscious defense mechanism in which the individual attributes to another person the unpleasant feelings or thoughts existing within himself.

Psychiatry—the specialized study and treatment of mental and emotional disturbances.

Psychoanalysis—a method of exploring the unconscious for research purposes and of making it conscious for therapeutic purposes.

Psychoneurosis—personality disorder due to emotional conflicts early in life, specifically involving unresolved conflicts during the Oedipal period.

Psychopath—a person who is emotionally unstable and who has no moral sense.

Psychosexual development—stages of libidinal growth and change.

Psychosis—severe, pathological mental disease or state.

Psychosomatic—condition in which the patient's feelings and emotional conflicts are converted or transformed so that they affect his body by actually involving the autonomic nervous system.

Psychotherapy—the use of psychological methods for treating mental and emotional disturbances.

Pyknic—in Kretschmer's terminology, those persons who possess a type of body build with large trunk, thick neck, and short legs. Kretschmer associated this build with the affective disorders.

Reactive depression—a depression without retardation or agitation developing in response to a situation in the patient's life.

Recurrent depression—a form of manic-depressive psychosis characterized by periods of depression alternating with periods of normality.

Recurrent manic—a form of manic-depressive psychosis characterized by periods of mania alternating with periods of normality.

Reference, ideas of—see *Ideas of reference.*

Regression—a psychoanalytic term denoting that the individual has returned to an earlier level of libidinal or psychosexual development.

Repression—mental process arising from conflict between the "pleasure principle" and the "reality principle," so that painful emotions are thrust into the unconscious.

Retardation—slowing up of movement producing underactivity with slow thinking and speech.

Retarded ejaculation—in men, the reaching of orgasm too late for satisfactory, enjoyable intercourse. See *Impotence.*

Sadism—sexual satisfaction or pleasure received from inflicting pain and suffering on others.

Schizoid—isolated, withdrawn personality.

Schizophrenia—serious mental disorder involving a split of the personality.

Sibling—brother or sister.

Stereotypy—frequent, almost mechanical repetition of the same posture, movement, or speech, as in the mannerisms associated with hebephrenic schizophrenia.

Stupor—state of extreme underactivity.

Sublimation—a mental mechanism in which an individual unconsciously deflects an unacceptable desire into a socially acceptable desire or activity.

Superego—conscience or moral sense.

Symbol—in psychoanalytic theory, an object or activity which can represent repressed feelings so that the real meaning may not be consciously recognized, as in dreams or in symptom formation.

Therapy—see *Psychotherapy*.

Tic—bizzare hypermotility.

Transference—emotional attitude directed from the patient to the psychoanalyst.

Traumatic—a term used to describe feelings the ego cannot handle, as in "traumatic event" or "traumatic neurosis."

Unconscious—anything concerning himself of which the individual is not aware.

Vaginal anethesia—a condition in which the vagina is unresponsive to stimulation. See *Frigidity*.

Vaginal stage—stage of psychosexual development reached by the mature woman when sexual interest is focused in the vagina.

Version—a term from Jungian psychology, describing the way in which the individual's emotions are directed. See *Extroversion; Introversion; Ambiversion*.

Wet dreams—see *Nocturnal emissions*.

Withdrawal—ego defense mechanism in which the individual turns into himself.

Index

171

Birth and development, 10-11
Bleuer, Eugen, 18n, 61-63
Blocks, learning, 152
Body build, 17-18, 76, 97
Bowel training, 21, 27
Brain
  degenerative process, 87
  diseases of, 86
    acute, 86
    chronic, 86-88
  organic brain syndromes, 7, 85-88
    nonpsychotics, 85-86, 88
    psychotic, 85-86, 88
    treatment, 89
  tumors, 87
Breaking and entering, 14
Breuer, J., 135
Bromide intoxication, 87

C

Cannon, W. B., 51
Castration complex, 34, 126
Catatonic, See Schizophrenia
Catharsis, 136
Cerea flexibilitas, 68-69
Cerebral arteriosclerosis, 88
Change of life, 100-101, 161-162
Character disorder, See Personality disorders
Charcot, J. M., 135, 136n
Chemotherapy, 77-78, 80-81, 89, 108, 132
Chromosomal damage, 84, 121
Circular recurrence, 94
Civil rights, 104
Classification of psychiatric diseases, 6-10
Clitoral stage, 24-26, 140, 143
Colitis, 137, 143
Collective unconscious, 18n
Coma, hypoglycemic, 77-78, 80
Commitment, 104
Communication, channels of, 155-156
Compensation, 26-28
Compensation neurosis, 133-134
Complex, inferiority, 50
  superiority, 50
Compromise, 51-54, 143, 155

Compulsion, 130-132
Compulsive-obsessional neurosis, 130-132
Concentration, difficulty, in, 65
Concretized thinking, 67
Conflict, 51-55
Congenital anomalies, 18-19
Conscience, 48
Conscious, 47, 49-50
Constipation, 137
Constitutional factors, 17-19
  body build, 17-18
  congenital anomalies, 18-19
  intelligence, 19
  version, 18
Contact with reality, 103-105
Conversion, 132, 137
Conversion neurosis, 132
Convulsions, 135
Crime, 114
Criminal responsibility, 104
Cunnilingus, 119
Curiosity, sexual, 38
Cyclothymic personality, 93

D

Dating, 154-155
Day-care program, 81
Death, 162
  reaction to, 108-111
Death wish, 30, 33-35, 39-40, 51
"Defective delinquents," 89
Defense mechanisms, 80, 125, 129, 143
  acting out, 8, 9, 120-121
  anankastic, 129-132
  compensation, 26-28
  compromise, 51-54, 143, 155
  conversion, 132, 137
  denial, 68-69, 80, 143
  displacement, 131
  emergency, 125, 127
  extrojection, 96, 143
  identification, 35, 40, 114-115, 123, 141, 143
  introjection, 96, 143
  isolation, 131
  projection, 69, 80, 143
  reaction formation, 26-28, 143

178